Math Mammoth
Grade 4-A Worktext

Grade 4·A Worktext

(A)ddition, subtraction, patterns, and graphs

(L)arge numbers

(M)ulti·digit multiplication

(T)ime and measuring

Light Blue Series

By Maria Miller

By Maria Miller

Contents

Chapter 3: Multi-Digit Multiplication

Chapter 4: Time and Measuring

Foreword

Math Mammoth Grade 4 comprises a complete math curriculum for the fourth grade mathematics studies. The curriculum meets and exceeds the Common Core standards.

The main areas of study in Math Mammoth Grade 4 are:

1. Students develop understanding and fluency with multi-digit multiplication, and use efficient multiplication procedures to solve problems.

2. They develop understanding of division to find quotients involving multi-digit dividends (long division), and they solve word problems involving division, including division with a remainder.

3. Students develop an understanding of fraction equivalence and some operations with fractions. They learn to add and subtract fractions with same denominators, and to multiply a fraction by a whole number.

4. Students learn the concept of angle. They draw and identify lines and angles, and classify shapes by properties of their lines and angles.

Additional topics we study are place value, time, measuring, graphs, and decimals.

This book, 4-A, covers addition and subtraction and graphs (chapter 1), place value (chapter 2), multi-digit multiplication (chapter 3), and time and measuring (chapter 4). The rest of the topics are covered in the 4-B worktext.

Some important points to keep in mind when using the curriculum:

- The two books (parts A and B) are like a "framework", but you still have a lot of liberty in planning the child's studies. Chapters 1, 2, and 3 should be studied in order, and Chapter 3 (multiplication) should be studied before Chapter 5 (division). However, you can be flexible with chapters 4 (time and measuring) and 6 (geometry), and schedule them earlier or later. Also, most lessons from chapters 7 and 8 (fractions and decimals) can be studied earlier; however the topic of finding parts with division should naturally be studied only after mastering division.

- Math Mammoth is mastery-based, which means it concentrates on a few major topics at a time, in order to study them in depth. However, you can still use it in a *spiral* manner, if you prefer. Simply have the child study in 2-3 chapters simultaneously. This type of flexible use of the curriculum enables you to truly individualize the instruction for the child.

- Don't automatically assign all the exercises. Use your judgment, trying to assign just enough for the child's needs. You can use the skipped exercises later for review. For most children, I recommend to start out by assigning about half of the available exercises. Adjust as necessary.

- For review, the curriculum includes a worksheet maker (Internet access required), mixed review lessons, additional cumulative review lessons, and the word problems continually require usage of past concepts. Please see more information about review (and other topics) in the FAQ at **https://www.mathmammoth.com/faq-lightblue.php**

I heartily recommend that you view the full user guide for your grade level, available at **https://www.mathmammoth.com/userguides/**

And lastly, you can find free videos matched to the curriculum at **https://www.mathmammoth.com/videos/**

I wish you success in teaching math!

Maria Miller, the author

Chapter 1: Addition, Subtraction, Patterns, and Graphs
Introduction

The first chapter of *Math Mammoth Grade 4* covers addition and subtraction, problem solving, patterns, graphs, and money. At first, we review the "technical aspects" of adding and subtracting: mental math techniques and adding and subtracting in columns. We also study some patterns. The lesson on Pascal's triangle is intended to be fun and fascinating—after all, Pascal's triangle is full of patterns!

In the next lesson, students use bar models (visual models with one or more horizontal "bars") to help them write addition and subtraction sentences with unknowns and to solve them. They are actually learning algebraic thinking and how to write and solve simple equations.

The lesson on the order of operations contains some review. We also connect this topic with real-life situations, such as shopping. The student writes simple expressions (number sentences) for word problems, which, again, practices algebraic thinking, and also helps students learn how to show their work in math problems. As applications of math, the chapter then contains straightforward lessons on bar graphs, line graphs, rounding, estimating, and money problems.

Keep in mind that the specific lessons in the chapter can take several days to finish. They are not "daily lessons." Instead, use the general guideline that fourth graders should finish about 2 pages daily or 9-11 pages a week. Also, I recommend not assigning all the exercises by default, but that you use your judgment, andtry to vary the number of assigned exercises according to the student's needs. See the user guide at https://www.mathmammoth.com/userguides/ for more guidance on using and pacing the curriculum.

Check out also the free videos matched to the curriculum at https://www.mathmammoth.com/videos/.

Helpful Resources on the Internet

Use these free online resources to supplement the "bookwork" as you see fit.

You can also access this list of links at https://l.mathmammoth.com/gr4ch1

THE BASIC OPERATIONS

Add Like Mad
Click on single-digit numbers that add up to the given sum as quickly as you can, clearing the board.
https://games.forkids.education/add-like-mad/

Sum Game
Click on numbers from the grid that add up to the target number.
https://www.transum.org/Software/Game/Sum_Game.asp

Sum Square
Fill in the intersecting boxes with numbers such that each box contains the required sum. Each level gets progressively more challenging.
https://www.mathnook.com/math/sum-square.html

Addition Mystery Picture
Reinforce your addition skills while uncovering a hidden picture.
https://www.mathmammoth.com/practice/mystery-picture#min=20&max=100

Subtraction Mystery Picture
Practice subtraction of two-digit numbers while uncovering a hidden picture.
https://www.mathmammoth.com/practice/mystery-picture-subtraction#min=11&max=100

Minus Mission
Practice subtraction facts within your chosen range, such as 0-12 or 0-20 while destroying green slime.
https://www.mathplayground.com/ASB_MinusMission.html

Make a Number
You have four operations and four numbers. Can you make the target number?
https://www.mathplayground.com/make_a_number.html

Math Mahjong Subtraction or Multiplication
Match tiles with the same value. Match all the tiles to win the game!
https://games.forkids.education/math-mahjong-subtraction/

https://games.forkids.education/math-mahjong-multiplication/

PATTERNS AND PASCAL'S TRIANGLE

Common Number Patterns
A list of the most common number patterns with illustrations and examples. Each section has a set of interactive practice questions.
https://www.mathsisfun.com/numberpatterns.html

Pascal's Triangle at Math Is Fun
Learn fascinating facts and patterns in Pascal's triangle!
https://www.mathsisfun.com/pascals-triangle.html

Pascal's Triangle Activity at Transum.org
Complete the Pascal's triangle. There are other levels of this activity that involve creating color patterns.
https://www.transum.org/Maths/Activity/Pascals/Triangle.asp

Coloring Multiples
Color various multiples (such as multiples of 6 or 10) in Pascal's Triangle, and see the patterns!
http://www.shodor.org/interactivate/activities/ColoringMultiples/

BAR MODELS AND PROBLEM SOLVING

Thinking Blocks - Addition and Subtraction
Model and solve word problems.
https://www.mathplayground.com/tb_addition/index.html

Jugs Puzzle — logical thinking puzzle
Fill and pour the water out of the two jugs until you get the desired quantity. Drag the jugs to empty or fill them.
https://www.mathsisfun.com/games/jugs-puzzle.html

Secret Code Addition Puzzle
Figure out the values of the symbols and solve the code!
https://www.mathplayground.com/secretcode_addition.html

Balancing Equations
Find the missing number to balance the calculations. Choose "Addition" and "Year 3".
https://mathsframe.co.uk/en/resources/resource/587/Balancing-Calculations

ORDER OF OPERATIONS

Choose Math Operation
Choose the operation(s) so that the given number sentence becomes true.
https://www.homeschoolmath.net/operation-game.php

Order of Operations Quiz
A 10-question online quiz that includes two different operations and possibly parentheses in each question. You can also modify the quiz parameters yourself.
https://www.thatquiz.org/tq-1/?-j8f-la

Order of Ops
Choose the expression to be solved in each step, and solve it. The program uses a visual representation of steps to show how the expression gets shorter at each step.
https://mrnussbaum.com/order-ops-online-game

The Order of Operations Millionaire
Answer multiple-choice questions that have to do with the order of operations, and win a million.
https://www.math-play.com/Order-of-Operations-Millionaire/order-of-operations-millionaire-game_html5.html

Exploring Order of Operations (Object Interactive)
Click on the operation to be done first in the given expression. The program then solves that, and you click on the *next* operation to be performed, etc., until it is solved. The resource also includes a game. Note: Loads slowly in Chrome, and doesn't work in Firefox.
https://www.learnalberta.ca/content/mejhm/html/object_interactives/order_of_operations/use_it.html

Order of Operations Practice
A simple online quiz of 10 questions. Uses parentheses and the four operations.
https://www.onlinemathlearning.com/order-of-operations-practice.html

ROUNDING AND ESTIMATING

Online Rounding Practice
Practice rounding to the nearest ten, hundred, or thousand.
https://www.mathmammoth.com/practice/rounding#number-range=0to10000&round-to=ten,hundred,thousand

Rounding to Thousands, Ten Thousands, or Hundred Thousands (Tutorialspoint.com)
Practice your rounding skills with this online multiple-choice quiz.
https://bit.ly/rounding-thousands

Rounding Sharks Game
Round numbers to the nearest hundred by clicking the shark with the correct rounded number.
https://www.free-training-tutorial.com/rounding/sharks.html

Town Creator Rounding
Practice rounding to the nearest ten, hundred, or thousand. Click on the correct answer to each problem to add a new house to your town. Unlock new levels to add trees, cars, and more!
https://www.free-training-tutorial.com/rounding/towncreator/tc-rounding.html

Ice Ice Maybe — fast estimation game
Help penguins migrate across a perilous ocean patrolled by killer whales. The game uses all operations.
https://www.mangahigh.com/en/games/iceicemaybe

Estimation Games
Find the answer fast! You also get points for being close. Choose "Add 100s" or "Add Tens" "Subtract Tens", or "Subtract 100s" for 4th graders.
https://www.mathsisfun.com/numbers/estimation-game.php

MONEY

Change Maker
Determine how many of each denomination you need to make the exact change. Choose the "hard" level for 4th graders. Playable in US, Canadian, Mexican, UK, or Australian money.
https://www.funbrain.com/games/change-maker

Cash Out
Give correct change by clicking on the bills and coins. It has three levels of difficulty.
https://mrnussbaum.com/cash-out-online-game

DATA AND GRAPHS

Bar Charts
Interactive questions about bar charts. First, choose a topic for the graph. Next, choose how the vertical axis is presented; for example, "20 intervals, 10 marked". Lastly, choose the type of questions asked.
https://www.topmarks.co.uk/Flash.aspx?f=barchartv2

Graphs Quiz
A 10-question online quiz that involves a variety of types of questions on line graphs, bar graphs, and pictograms. You can also easily change the quiz parameters to your liking.
https://www.thatquiz.org/tq-5/?-j50f15-l5-p0

Line Graphs at Maths Is Fun
A simple tutorial on line graphs, followed by ten interactive practice questions.
https://www.mathsisfun.com/data/line-graphs.html

Make a Bar Graph
Enter data into the bar graph, and your results are shown live.
https://www.mathsisfun.com/data/bar-graph.html

Graph Master
Create a graph from your own data (you can even make it up). The interactive activity creates the graph, and also makes up multiple-choice questions from your data for you to answer.
https://mrnussbaum.com/graphmaster

Addition Review

The numbers to be added are **addends**. The result is a **sum**. 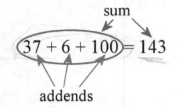 addends	You can write any number as a sum of its different parts: whole thousands, whole hundreds, whole tens, and ones. $5,248 = 5,000 + 200 + 40 + 8$ thousands hundreds tens ones $2,019 = 2,000 + 0 + 10 + 9$

You can add in parts (hundreds, tens, ones):	You can add in any order:	Trick: first add a bigger but easier number, then subtract to correct the error:
$56 + 124$ $= 100 + 50 + 20 + 6 + 4$ $= 100 + 70 + 10 = 180$	$7 + 90 + 91 + 3$ $= 7 + 3 + 90 + 91$ $= 10 + 90 + 91 = 191$	$76 + 89$ $= 76 + 90 - 1$ $= 166 - 1 = 165$

1. Add mentally. Compare the problems in each box!

a.	b.	c.	d.
$70 + 80 =$ __156__	$140 + 50 =$ __190__	$50 + 60 =$ __110__	$80 + 90 =$ __170__
$77 + 80 =$ __157__	$141 + 50 =$ __191__	$54 + 65 =$ __119__	$82 + 93 =$ __175__
$77 + 82 =$ __159__	$144 + 55 =$ __199__	$58 + 62 =$ __120__	$88 + 91 =$ __179__

2. Write each number as a sum of its parts: thousands, hundreds, tens, and ones.

a. $487 =$ __400+80+7__	**b.** $2,103 =$ __2,000+100+0+3__
c. $8,045 =$ __8,000+0+40+5__	**d.** $650 =$ __600+50+0__

3. Solve.

a. Emma added three numbers. Two of them were 56 and 90. The sum was 190. What was the third number she added?

b. The sum of four numbers is 70 and the sum of five other numbers is 80. What is the sum of all nine numbers?

4. Add and compare the sums. The addition problems are "related"!

a. 7 + 8 = _____	**b.** 4 + 9 = _____	**c.** 6 + 8 = _____
57 + 8 = _____	34 + 9 = _____	16 + 8 = _____
70 + 80 = _____	40 + 90 = _____	600 + 800 = _____
700 + 800 = _____	240 + 90 = _____	560 + 80 = _____

5. Write four different addition problems
   that are "related" to the problem 5 + 8 = 13.
   See examples above!

6. Add in any order, and in parts.

a. 80 + 5 + 2 + 30 + 4 + 44	**b.** 127 + 500 + 4 + 3 + 9 + 90

7. Find an easy way to add 99 to any number. (*Hint: It has to do with adding 100.*)
   Explain your idea, and add:

   a. 56 + 99   **b.** 487 + 99

8. Add mentally. You can add in parts (tens and ones separately) or use other "tricks."

a. 71 + 82 = _____	**b.** 42 + 47 = _____	**c.** 89 + 92 = _____
37 + 42 = _____	64 + 64 = _____	82 + 19 = _____
57 + 64 = _____	12 + 99 = _____	51 + 98 = _____

9. Find half and the double of the given numbers.

Half the number	*10*							
Number	20	90	110	120	480	900	1,600	4,010
Double the number	*40*							

10. **a.** The five people in the Brill family went to a
concert. The children's tickets were $20 each
and the two parents' tickets were $28 apiece.
What was the total cost of the tickets for the family?

    b. In another concert, a ticket for an adult ticket $30 and
tickets for children were half that price. What would
be the total cost of the tickets for the Brill family?

11. Fill in the table, adding 999 each time. *Hint: At first add 1,000, instead of 999. Then correct your answer.*

n	56	156	287	569	950	999
n + **999**						

12. Skip-count, starting from the number at the top, and adding the same number each time.

a. Start at 600. Add 600 each time:	**b.** Start at 900. Add 900 each time:	**c.** Start at 100. Add 75 each time:
1 2 0 0	_____	_____
_____	_____	_____
_____	_____	_____
_____	_____	_____
_____	_____	_____
What does this pattern remind you of?	What does this pattern remind you of?	_____
		_____

Adding in Columns

1. Add in columns. Check by adding the numbers in each column in a different order (for example, starting at the bottom and working up).

a.	**b.**	**c.**
	2 4 5	1 7 3 8
1 2	1 3 9	2 3 9 0
1 3 8 4	3 0	1 0 7 8
2 9 1 2	2 9 3 1	3 6 4
2 0 0 8	5 9 4	2 8 0 3
2 0 9	4 5 9 3	2 1 1
+ 2 6	+ 5 2 6	+ 9 9
5,539		

2. Add. Write the numbers under each other, carefully aligning the ones, tens, hundreds, and thousands. You may use a separate piece of paper if you prefer.

   a. 5,609 + 1,388 + 89 + 402 + 837

   b. 67 + 504 + 1,298 + 492 + 3,288 + 8

3. The map shows some Kentucky cities and distances between them.

   The two distances that may be hard to read are: from Louisville to Frankfort is 54 miles; from Frankfort to Lexington is 28 miles.

   Calculate the total driving distance, if a family goes on a trip like this:

   a. Covington - Lexington - Paducah - Lexington - Covington

   b. A trip from Lexington via Covington, Louisville, and Frankfort, and back to Lexington.

Subtraction Review

<table>
<tr><td>Compare the methods.</td><td>Marie: "I subtract in parts: first to the previous whole ten, then the rest."

35 − 7

= (35 − 5) − 2

=   30 − 2 = 28</td><td>John: "I use a helping problem."

15 − 7 = 8 is the helping problem for 35 − 7.

The answer to 35 − 7 also ends in "8" and is in the previous ten (the twenties). So, 35 − 7 is 28.</td></tr>
</table>

1. Subtract.

a.	b.	c.	d.
13 − 7 = _6_	12 − 6 = _6_	15 − 9 = _6_	16 − 8 = _8_
63 − 7 = _56_	82 − 6 = _76_	150 − 90 = _60_	1,600 − 800 = _800_

2. Subtract from whole hundreds. You can subtract in parts.

a.	b.	c.	d.
100 − 2 = _98_	200 − 4 = _196_	500 − 5 = _495_	400 − 7 = _393_
100 − 20 = _80_	200 − 40 = _60_	500 − 50 = _450_	400 − 70 = _430_
100 − 22 = _78_	200 − 45 = _55_	500 − 56 = _444_	400 − 71 = _429_

3. Subtract and compare the results. The problems are "related" — can you see how?

a. 12 − 8 = _4_	b. 15 − 9 = _6_	c. 13 − 7 = _6_
42 − 8 = _34_	75 − 9 = _66_	73 − 7 = _66_
120 − 80 = _40_	150 − 90 = _60_	1,300 − 700 = _600_
520 − 80 = _440_	650 − 90 = _560_	430 − 70 = _360_

4. Write here four different subtraction problems that are "related" to the problem 14 − 8 = 6. See the examples above!

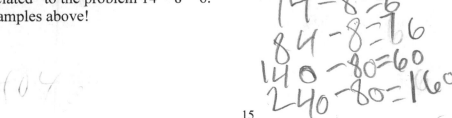

14 − 8 = 6
84 − 8 = 76
140 − 80 = 60
240 − 80 = 160

15

Trick: Instead of subtracting 99, subtract 100! Then correct the error: you subtracted 1 too much, so add 1 to the result.	$705 - 99$ $= 705 - 100 + 1$ $= 605 + 1 = 606$	$140 - 88$ $= 140 - 90 + 2$ $= 50 + 2 = 52$

5. Fill in the table, subtracting 99 each time.

n	125	293	404	487	640	849
$n - 99$						

Strategy: Add up to find the difference of two numbers.		
To solve $93 - 28$, start at 28 and add until you reach 93. However much you added is the difference.	$+\boxed{2}$ $+\boxed{60}$ $+\boxed{3}$ $28 \quad 30 \qquad 90 \quad 93$ $93 - 28 = \underline{(2 + 60 + 3)} = \underline{65}$	$+\boxed{40}$ $+\boxed{200}$ $+\boxed{20}$ $160 \quad 200 \qquad 400 \quad 420$ $420 - 160 = \underline{(40 + 200 + 20)} = \underline{260}$

6. Subtract mentally in parts, use a helping problem, add up to find the difference, or use other "tricks".

a. $91 - 82 =$ _____ $42 - 37 =$ _____ $77 - 64 =$ _____	**b.** $100 - 82 =$ _____ $100 - 56 =$ _____ $96 - 48 =$ _____	**c.** $56 - 29 =$ _____ $61 - 39 =$ _____ $84 - 38 =$ _____
d. $250 - 180 =$ _____ $440 - 390 =$ _____ $730 - 290 =$ _____	**e.** $1,000 - 555 =$ _____ $1,000 - 56 =$ _____ $1,000 - 208 =$ _____	**f.** $500 - 82 =$ _____ $612 - 70 =$ _____ $540 - 48 =$ _____

7. **a.** Fill in the table, subtracting 27 each time, and continue the pattern.

n	120	140	160	180	200				
$n - 27$									

b. What pattern(s) do you notice in the second row?

8. Skip-count backwards. In other words, subtract the same number repeatedly.

a. Start at 240. Subtract 40 each time:	b. Start at 5,400. Subtract 600 each time:	c. Start at 490. Subtract 70 each time:
_____	_____	_____
_____	_____	_____
_____	_____	_____
_____	_____	_____
_____	_____	_____
_____	_____	_____
What does this pattern remind you of?	What does this pattern remind you of?	What does this pattern remind you of?

9. Repeated Subtraction Game

In this game, you pair number cards together, two by two. With each two cards, you subtract the smaller number as many times as possible from the bigger number. For example, Jane pairs together cards 20 and 4. Jane subtracts 20 − 4 − 4 − 4 − 4 − 4 = 0. Jim pairs the cards 45 and 11, and subtracts 45 − 11 − 11 − 11 − 11 = 1. He can't subtract any more.

Each player gets as many "points" as is the "remainder" number (the final difference). Above, Jane got 0 points and Jim got 1. The first player to accumulate 25 points *loses* the game.

(1) Write the subtractions that Jane does with these cards:

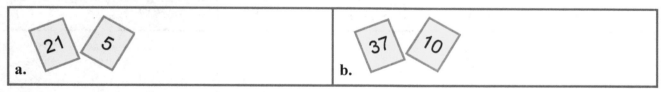

a.

b.

(2) Now create two pairs of cards (using all four cards). Choose the pairs so that you will get the least possible points for each pair. Lastly, add to get your final points.

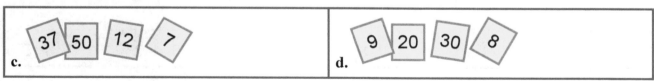

c.

d.

e. Play the game yourself! Try number cards from 2-30 for an easier game. Try numbers from 2 to 60 for a challenge. Give each player 4-8 cards, depending on the difficulty level you want.

Subtract in Columns

You cannot regroup a ten or a hundred. So regroup 1 thousand as 10 hundreds.

```
  6  10
  7  0  2
-4 9  3  3
```

Next, regroup one of the hundreds as 10 tens.

```
       9
  6  10  10
  7  0   2
-4 9  3  3
```

Lastly, regroup one of the tens as 10 ones (there are already 2 ones so you get 12).

```
       9   9
  6  10  10  12
  7  0   0   2
-4 9  3   3
────────────
  2  0   6   9
```

1. Subtract in columns. Check by adding!

a.	Add to check:	b.	Add to check:	c.	Add to check:
5 1 9 − 3 4 6	+ 3 4 6	6 5 2 8 − 2 7 1 9	+ 2 7 1 9	1 3 5 0 − 7 8 2	+ 7 8 2
d.	Add to check:	**e.**	Add to check:	**f.**	Add to check:
7 0 0 − 3 5 6	+ 3 5 6	5 1 0 2 − 1 3 3 8	+ 1 3 3 8	6 1 0 4 − 7 7 8	+ 7 7 8
g.	Add to check:	**h.**	Add to check:	**i.**	Add to check:
5 0 6 − 2 8 9	+ 2 8 9	4 0 9 0 − 3 7 8 5	+ 3 7 8 5	9 0 0 0 − 3 4 2 0	+ 3 4 2 0

8,120 − 2,653 − 754 = ?	$\begin{array}{r} \scriptstyle 7\ \ 10\ 11\ 10 \\ \cancel{8}\ \ \cancel{1}\ \ \cancel{2}\ \ \cancel{0} \\ -\ 2\ \ 6\ \ 5\ \ 3 \\ \hline \end{array}$	Check:	

When subtracting two numbers, you can continue the subtraction under your first answer.

Check by adding the answer and all the numbers you subtracted.

$$\begin{array}{r} 5\ 4\ 6\ 7 \\ -\quad 7\ 5\ 4 \\ \hline 4\ 7\ 1\ 3 \end{array}$$

Check:
$$\begin{array}{r} 4\ 7\ 1\ 3 \\ 7\ 5\ 4 \\ +\ 2\ 6\ 5\ 3 \\ \hline 8\ 1\ 2\ 0 \end{array}$$

2. Write the numbers under each other carefully, and subtract. Lastly, check by adding.

a. 4,400 − 2,745 − 493	**a.** Add to check	**b.** 5,604 − 592 − 87	**b.** Add to check

3. You can solve the problem 5,200 − 592 − 87 − 345 − 99 by subtracting the numbers one at a time. That means four separate subtractions. Find a quicker way, and use it to solve this problem.

4. Look again at the Kentucky map, and solve the problems.

Kentucky

a. Mr. Jefferson travels from Paducah to Lexington and back, three times a month. What is the total mileage he travels?

b. Compare the round trip from Lexington to Ashland and back with the round trip from Lexington to Covington and back. How much longer is the first than the second?

Puzzle Corner Little Hannah has almost learned to read the (analog) clock, but she can't remember which hand is the hour hand and which is the minute hand. So when the time is 1:15, she might say, "It is 3:05", mixing the hours and the minutes.

Which is which?

One day Mom was lying in bed, and she asked Hannah what time it was. Hannah said, "It is 2:20." Just a few minutes later Mom asked again for the time. Hannah claimed it was now 4:25.

Remembering that each time Hannah either tells the time right, or mixes the hour and minute hands, Mom was able to figure out what time it was *in reality*. Can you?

Patterns and Mental Math

1. **a.** First, fill in the top row, continuing the pattern it has. Then add 29 to each number in the top row to get the number in the bottom row. *Hint: Instead of adding 29, add 30, and subtract 1!*

n	9	18	27	36	45	54				
$n + 29$	_38_									

   b. What skip-counting pattern does the top row have?

   c. Does the bottom row have any skip-counting pattern?

2. **a.** First, fill in the top row, continuing the pattern it has. Then subtract 39 from each number in the top row to get the number in the bottom row. *Hint: Instead of subtracting 39, subtract ___, and add __!*

n	660	600	540	480	420			
$n - 39$								

   b. What skip-counting pattern does the top row have?

   c. Does the bottom row have any skip-counting pattern?

3. Subtract mentally. Compare the problems in each box—and be careful!

a.	**b.**	**c.**
$500 - 3 =$ _____	$600 - 2 =$ _____	$1,000 - 7 =$ _____
$500 - 30 =$ _____	$600 - 20 =$ _____	$1,000 - 70 =$ _____
$500 - 300 =$ _____	$600 - 200 =$ _____	$1,000 - 700 =$ _____
$500 - 33 =$ _____	$600 - 22 =$ _____	$1,000 - 77 =$ _____
$500 - 303 =$ _____	$600 - 202 =$ _____	$1,000 - 707 =$ _____

4. Figure out the patterns and continue them.

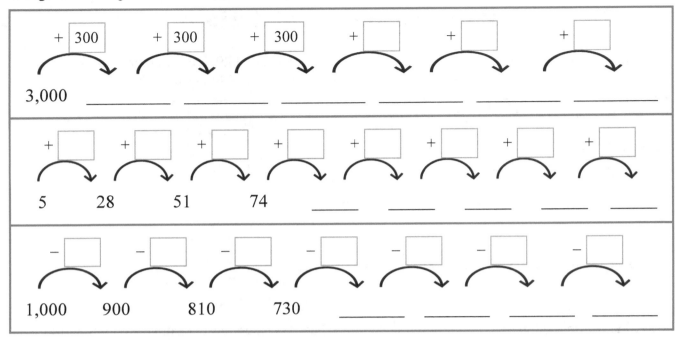

5. Figure out an easy way to subtract 999 from any number mentally.
   For example, explain how to easily subtract 1,446 − 999.

6. Solve the problems.

a. One alarm clock costs $11 and another costs $8 more than the first. How much would the two cost together?
b. It rained five days in June and six days in July. How many days did it *not* rain in those two months (in total)?
c. Amy is 134 cm tall and her mom is 162 cm tall. What is the difference in their heights?
d. Jack rode his bicycle 28 kilometers on Tuesday and on Wednesday. On Thursday and Saturday he rode along a route that was 6 kilometers shorter. How many kilometers did he ride in total during those four days?
e. Of the 45 students, 18 are girls. How many more boys are there than girls?

Patterns in Pascal's Triangle

1. Fill in **Pascal's triangle**. The blocks on the furthest left and right have the number 1 in them. To find the number for any other block, *add* the two numbers right above it (slightly to the right and to the left). For example, the colored number 3 comes from adding the 1 and 2 above it.

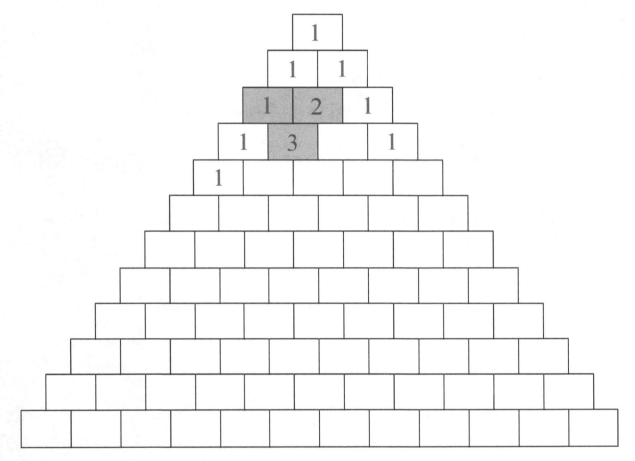

2. After filling in the triangle, add the numbers in each row and make a list.

The sum of row 1: _____1_____   The sum of row 7: _____

The sum of row 2: _____2_____   The sum of row 8: _____

The sum of row 3: _____4_____   The sum of row 9: _____

The sum of row 4: _____   The sum of row 10: _____

The sum of row 5: _____   The sum of row 11: _____

The sum of row 6: _____   The sum of row 12: _____

What do you notice about the sums of each row?

3. Can you find a *diagonal* with the numbers 1, 2, 3, 4, 5, 6, 7?
   (A diagonal is a line through a shape from corner to corner, such as in a square.)

4. *Triangular numbers* start like this:

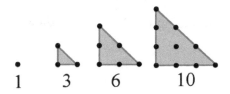

1   3   6   10

   a. Continue the pattern of triangular numbers.

   b. Find a diagonal with triangular numbers in Pascal's triangle.

   c. Can you find something special about the triangular numbers?
   (Hint: It has to do with how much each number differs from the previous number.)

5. Below you will find an empty Pascal's triangle to explore with. You can fill it in with some other
   number on all the sides, such as 2, 3, or 20.

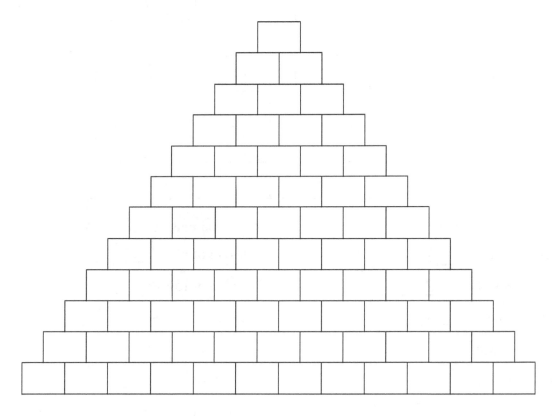

Read more about Pascal's triangle and its patterns at **https://ptri1.tripod.com/**

Bar Models in Addition and Subtraction

Think of this **bar model** as a long board, cut into two pieces. It is 56 units long in total, and the two parts are 15 and x units long.

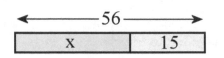

From the bar model, we can write <u>two</u> addition and <u>two</u> subtraction sentences—a **fact family**.

The x stands for a number, too. We just don't know what it is yet. It is an **unknown**.

$x + 15 = 56$	$56 - x = 15$
$15 + x = 56$	$56 - 15 = x$

From this bar model, we can write a **missing addend** problem. It means that a number to be added is "missing" or unknown:

$$769 + x = 1,510$$

We can solve it by subtracting the one part (769) from the total (1,510).

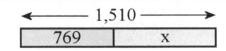

$$769 + x = 1,510$$

$$x = 1,510 - 769 = 741$$

1. Write a missing addend problem that matches the bar model. Then solve it by subtracting.

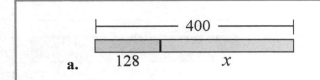

a.

_____ + _____ = _____

$x =$ _____ − _____ = _____

b.

_____ + _____ = _____

$x =$ _____ − _____ = _____

c. A car costs \$1,200. Dad has \$890. How much more does he need to buy it?

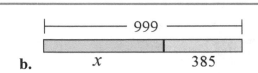

_____ + _____ = _____

$x =$ _____ − _____ = _____

d. The school has 547 students, of which 265 are girls. How many are boys?

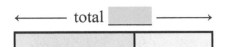

_____ + _____ = _____

$x =$ _____ − _____ = _____

2. Add the given numbers *and* the unknown *x* to the bar model. Note, *x* is the unknown, or what the problem asks for. Then write an addition (a missing addend problem) and solve it.

a. Of their 1,200-mile trip, the Jones family traveled 420 miles yesterday and 370 miles today. How many miles do they have left to travel?

Addition:

Solution: *x* = _____

b. The store is expecting a shipment of 4,000 blank CDs. Three boxes of 400 arrived. How many CDs are yet to come?

Addition:

Solution: *x* = _____

c. A 250-cm board is divided into three parts: two 28-cm parts at the ends and a part in the middle. How long is the middle part?

Addition:

Solution: *x* = _____

d. After traveling 56 miles, Dad said, "Okay, in 9 miles we will be at Kensville, and from there we will have 118 miles left." How many miles in total is the trip?

Addition:

Solution: *x* = _____

3. Make a word problem that matches the model. Then solve for *x*.

x	1,750

4,900

x = _____

In this subtraction problem, $x - 170 = 560$, the *total* is unknown. (Remember, subtraction problems start with the total.) Look at the bar model. We can solve x by adding.	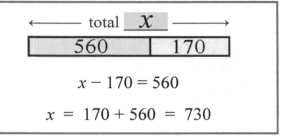 $x - 170 = 560$ $x = 170 + 560 = 730$

4. Write a subtraction problem that matches the bar model. Then solve it by adding.

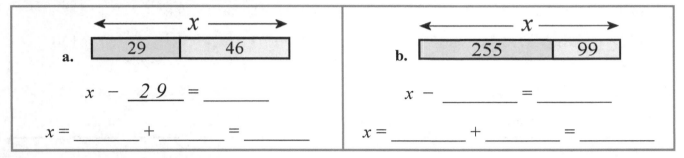

a. $x - \underline{29} = \underline{}$

$x = \underline{} + \underline{} = \underline{}$

b. $x - \underline{} = \underline{}$

$x = \underline{} + \underline{} = \underline{}$

5. The number you are subtracting from is missing! Solve.

a. $\underline{} - 4 = 20$	b. $\underline{} - 15 = 17$	c. $\underline{} - 22 - 7 = 70$

Still, the number you are subtracting from is missing. This time, it is denoted by x, not by an empty line.

d. $x - 8 = 7$ $x = \underline{}$	e. $x - 24 = 48$ $x = \underline{}$	f. $x - 300 - 50 = 125$ $x = \underline{}$

6. The number you subtract here is the unknown. Write the numbers and x in the bar model. Notice carefully which number is the *total*. Then write a subtraction that helps you solve x.

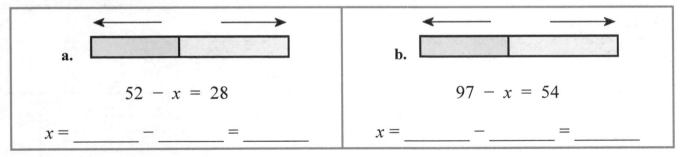

a. $52 - x = 28$

$x = \underline{} - \underline{} = \underline{}$

b. $97 - x = 54$

$x = \underline{} - \underline{} = \underline{}$

7. The number you subtract is still the unknown. Solve.

a. $20 - \underline{} = 12$	b. $55 - \underline{} = 34$	c. $234 - \underline{} = 100$
d. $61 - x = 43$ $x = \underline{}$	e. $100 - x = 72$ $x = \underline{}$	f. $899 - x = 342$ $x = \underline{}$

8. Circle the number sentence that fits the problem. Then solve for x.

a. Jane had \$15. After Dad gave Jane her allowance (x), Jane had \$22. $\$15 + x = \$22$ OR $\$15 + \$22 = x$ $x =$ _____	**b.** Mike had many drawings. He put 24 of them in the trash. Then he had 125 left. $125 - 24 = x$ OR $x - 24 = 125$ $x =$ _____
c. Jill had 120 marbles, but some of them got lost. Now she has 89 left. $120 - x = 89$ OR $120 + 89 = x$ $x =$ _____	**d.** Dave gave 67 of his stickers to a friend and now he has 150 left. $150 - 67 = x$ OR $x - 67 = 150$ $x =$ _____

9. Write a number sentence (addition or subtraction) with x. Solve it.

a. The 43 teachers and all the students of a school filled a 450-seat auditorium. How many students does the school have?	_____ + _____ = _____ $x =$ _____
b. Mom went shopping with \$250 and had \$78 when she came home. How much did she spend?	originally − spent = left _____ − _____ = _____ $x =$ _____
c. Janet had \$200. Then she bought an item for \$54 and another for \$78. How much money does she have now?	_____ − _____ − _____ = _____ $x =$ _____
d. Jean bought one item for \$23 and another for \$29, and she had \$125 left. How much money did she have initially?	_____ − _____ − _____ = _____ $x =$ _____

Puzzle Corner	Find the missing numbers.	
a. $200 - 45 -$ _____ $- 70 = 25$	**b.** _____ $- 5 - 55 - 120 = 40$	
c. $23 + 56 + x = 110$ $x =$ _____	**d.** $x + 15 + 15 + 15 + 15 = 97$ $x =$ _____	

Order of Operations

1. Do operations within ( ) first.
 	
2. Then multiply and divide, from left to right.
 	
3. Then add and subtract, from left to right.
    In the examples, the operation
    to be done first is colored.
	$60 - 21 \div 3 + 5$
	$= 60 - 7 + 5$
	$= 53 + 5$
	$= 58$
		$4 + 3 \times (6 - 2)$
		$= 4 + 3 \times 4$
		$= 4 + 12$
		$= 16$

1. Calculate in the right order. Hint: circle the operation(s) to be done first (as if in a "balloon").

a. $2 \times (5 + 3) = $ _____	**b.** $2 \times 5 + 6 \div 2 = $ _____	**c.** $2 \times 5 + 9 \div 1 = $ _____
d. $20 - 3 \times 3 = $ _____	**e.** $(10 - 3) \times 3 + 1 = $ _____	**f.** $2 + (20 - 16) \times 3 = $ _____
g. $9 - 1 - 8 \div 2 = $ _____	**h.** $2 \times (2 + 2) - 3 = $ _____	**i.** $50 - 1 \times 7 + 2 \times 3 = $ _____

2. You cut off two 20-cm pieces of a 90-cm piece of wood.
   Which calculation tells you the length of the piece that is left?

   $90 - 20 + 20$ $90 - 2 \times 20$ $(90 - 20) \times 2$

3. James feeds his dogs 5 kg of dog food daily.
   He bought a 100-kg bag of dog food.
   How many kilograms are left after four days?
   Write a *single* number sentence to solve that.

4. Parking costs $2 per hour during the day and $3 per hour
   during the night. Write a single number sentence that tells
   you the cost of parking a car for 5 daytime hours and
   2 nighttime hours. Solve it.

5. Put operation symbols +, − , or × into the number sentences so that they become true.

a. $4 \square 1 \square 8 = 12$	**b.** $2 \square 10 \square 1 \square 2 = 14$	**c.** $3 \square 3 \square 3 = 6$

Notice: Whether you subtract a sum of several numbers → $100 - (40 + 20 + 30) = 10$

or subtract the numbers one by one → $100 - 40 - 20 - 30 = 10$

...the answer is the same!

Example. You buy items that cost $9, $5, and $12. You pay with $50.

To find the change you get, you could subtract the numbers one by one from fifty: $50 - 9 - 5 - 12$.

But it is easier to first *add* $9 + 5 + 12 = 26$ to get the total cost, and then subtract $50 - 26 = 24$. This last method can also be written as $50 - (9 + 5 + 12) = 24$.

6. Find the problems that have the same answer. You don't have to calculate the answers.

a. $500 - 30 - 30$	**b.** $250 + (100 - 50)$	**c.** $8{,}000 - (2{,}500 + 800 + 300)$
$500 - 30 + 30$	$250 + 100 - 50$	$8{,}000 - 2{,}500 + 800 + 300$
$500 - (30 + 30)$	$250 - 100 - 50$	$8{,}000 - 2{,}500 - 800 - 300$

7. A clerk in a store rings up all the items the customer buys, and figures out the change.

   Which calculation on the right gives you the the amount of change the customer receives?

   (You don't have to calculate the answer.)

   a. $\$50 - \$1.26 - \$6.55 - \$0.22 - \$5$

   b. $\$50 + \$1.26 + \$6.55 + \$0.22 + \$5$

   c. $\$50 - (\$1.26 + \$6.55 + \$0.22 + \$5)$

8. Describe a shopping situation where you need to do this calculation:

   $\$10 - 4 \times \$1.20$

9. Calculate.

a. $20 + 30 \div (2 + 3) = $ _____	**b.** $7 \times (5 + 6) \div 7 = $ _____	**c.** $32 - 8 + 5 + 20 \div 5 = $ _____
$200 - 3 - 3 - 3 = $ _____	$120 - (60 - 50) \times 2 = $ _____	$(20 - 16) \times 3 + 2 = $ _____

10. Put operation symbols $+$, $-$, or $\times$ into the number sentences so that they become true.

a. $50 \;\square\; 5 \;\square\; 10 = 0$	**b.** $100 \;\square\; (15 \;\square\; 17) \;\square\; 1 = 68$	**c.** $(2 \;\square\; 5) \;\square\; 2 = 14$

*See also the **Choose Two Operations** game at* https://www.homeschoolmath.net/operation-game.php

Making Bar Graphs

1. Beverly asked her classmates how many hours they watch TV each day.
   The results are below; she already organized them in order.

   0 0 1 1 1 1 1 1 1 1 1 1 1 2 2 2 2 3 3 3 3 4 4 4 5 5 6

Each number above is someone's answer to Beverly's question. For example, two people answered that they watch TV for 0 hours. Quite a few answered that they watch TV for 1 hour each day.

With so many numbers, we need to first make a **frequency table**. In it, we write <u>how frequently</u> or <u>how often</u> each number appears in the data. After that, we can make a bar graph.

a. In Beverly's data above, the number zero (0 hours of TV) appeared two times. The number two (2 hours of TV) appeared four times. Finish the frequency table and the bar graph.

Hours of TV	Frequency
0 h	2
1 h	
2 h	4

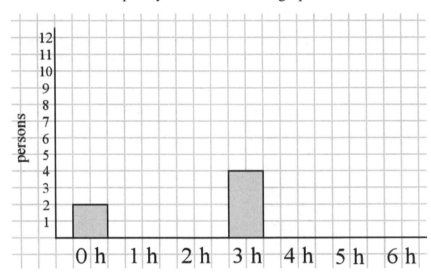

b. How many classmates did Beverly question?

c. What was the most common response to Beverly's question?

d. How many of these children watch TV one hour or less?

e. How many watch TV three hours or more?

f. Are there more children who watch TV three hours than those who watch it two hours a day?

g. Are there more children who watch TV two or more hours than children who watch TV less than two hours a day?

2. **a.** Beverly also asked some people about their favorite color. Make a bar graph.

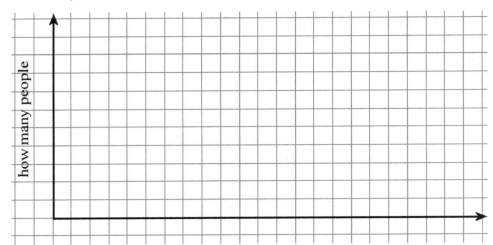

Color	Frequency
red	2
orange	1
yellow	4
green	5
blue	7
purple	4
black	2
white	2

b. How many people did Beverly question?

c. Were the "warm" colors or the "cold" colors more popular?
(Warm colors are red, orange, and yellow. Cold colors are green, blue, and purple.)

3. These numbers are students' quiz scores: 1 3 5 3 6 4 9 8 6 4 8 7 5 3 9 8 6 2 1 8 9 10 2 9 7 6

a. Make a frequency table and a bar graph.

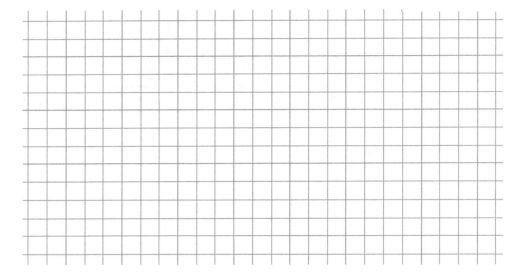

Test score	Frequency

b. What was the most common quiz score?   How many students got that score?

c. What was the least common quiz score?   How many students got that score?

d. How many students got a score from five to eight?

e. How many students did excellent (got a score of nine or 10)?

f. The teacher said after the test, "Anyone with a score of four or less will need to retake the test." How many students need to take the test again?

Line Graphs

A line graph shows how something changes over *time*, for example over hours, days, weeks, months, or years. The data values are often drawn as dots and then the dots are connected with lines.

A line graph has a horizontal axis (*x*-axis in the picture), and a vertical axis (*y*-axis). The horizontal axis is for the time units.

To read a line graph, look "up" from a time unit until you find a dot. Then draw an imaginary line from that dot to the vertical or *y*-axis, and read the value at that axis.

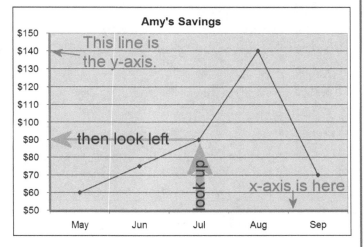

We can see that In July, Amy had $90 in her savings.

1. **a.** How many dollars did Amy have in her savings in May?

   b. How many dollars did Amy have in her savings in August?

   c. In which month did she have $75 in her savings?

   d. How many dollars did Amy add to her savings from June to July?

   e. How much less did Amy have in her savings in September than in August? What could have caused that?

2. The graph shows a puppy's weight for 10 days after birth. Notice how the two axes are named as "Day" and "grams".

   a. About how many grams did the puppy weigh on day 1? _____

   Day 2? _____

   Day 3? _____

   Day 4? _____

   b. What is the first day that the puppy weighed 600 g or more?

   c. What is the first day that the puppy weighed 700 g or more?

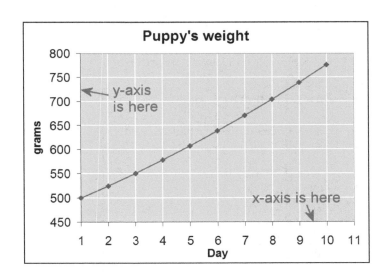

3. Look at the graph of the monthly prices of strawberries, given in dollars per pound.
   The *retail* price is the price you see in a grocery store (the price customers pay).

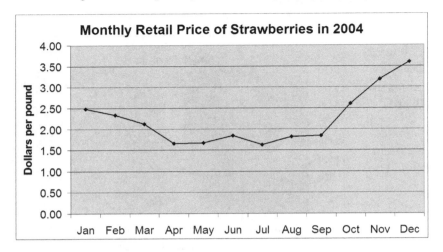

Month	Price ($ per lb)
Jan	2.48
Feb	2.33
Mar	2.12
Apr	1.66
May	1.67
Jun	1.85
Jul	1.63
Aug	1.82
Sep	1.84
Oct	2.60
Nov	3.19
Dec	3.60

a. How does the price change from winter to summer?

Why is it that way?

b. Find the highest price per pound and the lowest price per pound.
   What is the *difference* of these two?

c. How much did it cost to buy 2 lb of strawberries in August?   In November?

4. Rebecca's mom wrote down an "x" mark for any bad behavior she showed during the day.
   The table shows the list of her x-marks.

   a. Make a line graph. Remember, the one axis is "days" and the other is "x-marks."

   b. Did Rebecca's behavior improve?

Day	x-marks
Mon	10
Tue	8
Wed	9
Thu	6
Fri	3
Sat	4
Sun	2

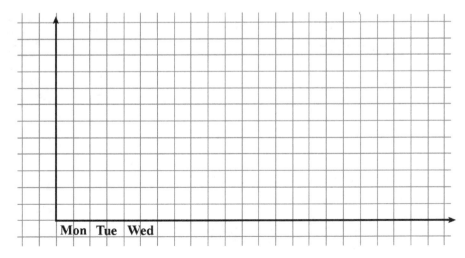

5. The table gives the average maximum temperatures for each month in New York.

Month	Max. Temp.	Month	Max. Temp.	Month	Max. Temp.
Jan	3°C	May	20°C	Sep	26°C
Feb	3°C	Jun	25°C	Oct	21°C
Mar	7°C	Jul	28°C	Nov	11°C
Apr	14°C	Aug	27°C	Dec	5°C

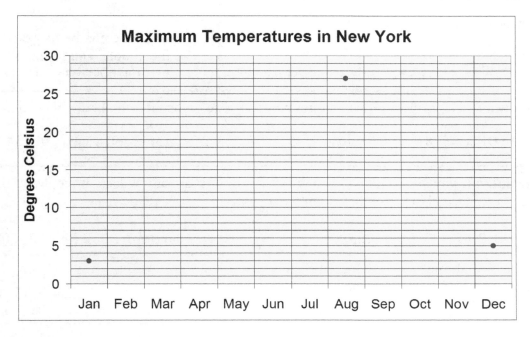

a. Make a line graph. Three values are already done for you.

b. What are the three coldest months?

c. What are the four warmest months?

d. What is the difference in maximum temperature between the coldest and the warmest month?

6. Make a line graph from some data that you gather yourself! Just remember, it has to be something that changes over *time*. You can also "make up" your own data. Here are some ideas:

• the outside temperature from the morning till the evening

• your savings, or an imaginary child's savings, in 6, 8, or 12 months

• how many hours of schoolwork (or housework or playing) you do each day of the week

• how many pages of a book you read each day during a week

• your height from year zero to year nine of your life

You can also use this neat online tool for creating your graph:
https://nces.ed.gov/nceskids/createagraph/
To use it, you need to have your data ready. It will not give you any data. It just draws the graph.

Rounding

When you are rounding to the nearest *ten*, look at the ONES DIGIT of the number.

- If the ones digit is 0, 1, 2, 3, or 4, then round down.

- If the ones digit is 5, 6, 7, 8, or 9, then round up.

- If you round up, the tens digit increases by one.

The sign " ≈ " is read "is about", or "is approximately".

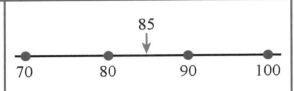

When the number is exactly in the middle, **round up**. 85 ≈ 90.
(This is just conventional.)

You can draw a line after the digit you are rounding to. The digits after the line will become zeros.

| 25⦙6 ≈ 26⦙0 (up) | 8⦙4 ≈ 8⦙0 (down) | 3,28⦙7 ≈ 3,29⦙0 (up) | 9,85⦙4 ≈ 9,85⦙0 (down) |

Notice carefully: If you are rounding up, and the tens digit is already 9, look at the *two* digits just before your line, and increase that "number" by one:

| 3,29⦙7 ≈ 3,30⦙0 (up) | 79⦙5 ≈ 80⦙0 (up) | 3,09⦙8 ≈ 3,10⦙0 (up) |
| It is as if the "29" formed by the hundreds and tens changes into "30"—exactly one more. (In reality it is "29" tens changing to "30" tens.) | The "79" changes to "80". | The "09" changes to "10". |

1. Round the numbers to the nearest ten. The number line can help.

a. 294 ≈ _____   b. 315 ≈ _____   c. 278 ≈ _____   d. 285 ≈ _____

e. 322 ≈ _____   f. 296 ≈ _____   g. 304 ≈ _____   h. 207 ≈ _____

2. Round these numbers to the nearest ten.

a. 526 ≈ _____   b. 34 ≈ _____   c. 181 ≈ _____

d. 197 ≈ _____   e. 705 ≈ _____   f. 392 ≈ _____

g. 440 ≈ _____   h. 5,971 ≈ _____   i. 9,568 ≈ _____

j. 4,061 ≈ _____   k. 2,282 ≈ _____   l. 4,003 ≈ _____

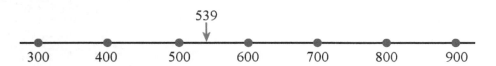

539

Find the whole hundred that is nearest to 539. Rounded to the nearest hundred, 539 ≈ _____.

When you are rounding to the nearest *hundred*, look at the TENS DIGIT.

- If the tens digit is 0, 1, 2, 3, or 4, then round down.
- If the tens digit is 5, 6, 7, 8, or 9, then round up.
- The rounded result is a whole hundred so it ends in two zeros.
- The hundreds digit changes by one if you round up.

You can draw a line after the digit you are rounding to. The digits after the line will become zeros.

| 5 6 2 ≈ 6 0 0 | 2 4 8 ≈ 2 0 0 (down) | 1,2 9 0 ≈ 1,3 0 0 (up) | 5,4 2 8 ≈ 5,4 0 0 (down) |

Notice carefully: If you are rounding up, and the hundreds digit is already 9, look at the *two* digits just before your line, and increase that "number" by one:

| 5,9 9 2 ≈ 6,0 0 0 (up) | 6,9 7 1 ≈ 7,0 0 0 (up) | 12,9 6 1 ≈ 13,0 0 0 (up) |
| It is as if the "59" formed by the thousands and hundreds changes into "60"—exactly one more. | The "69" changes to "70". | The "29" changes to "30". |

3. Round the numbers to the nearest hundred.

a. 3,520 ≈ _____

b. 3,709 ≈ _____

c. 3,935 ≈ _____

d. 3,541 ≈ _____

e. 3,962 ≈ _____

f. 3,425 ≈ _____

4. Round these numbers to the nearest hundred.

a. 526 ≈ _____

b. 54 ≈ _____

c. 761 ≈ _____

d. 197 ≈ _____

e. 706 ≈ _____

f. 365 ≈ _____

g. 2,907 ≈ _____

h. 5,971 ≈ _____

i. 7,543 ≈ _____

j. 3,032 ≈ _____

k. 2,959 ≈ _____

l. 4,014 ≈ _____

4,772

Rounded to the nearest thousand, 4,772 ≈ 5,000.

When you are rounding to the nearest *thousand*, look at the HUNDREDS DIGIT.
- If the hundreds digit is 0, 1, 2, 3, or 4, then round down.
- If the hundreds digit is 5, 6, 7, 8, or 9, then round up.
- The rounded result is a whole thousand so it ends in three zeros.
- The thousands digit changes by one if you round up.

You can draw a line after the thousands digit. The digits after the line will become zeros.

2,723 ≈ 3,000 (up)   9,804 ≈ 10,000 (up)   7,288 ≈ 7,000 (down)   457 ≈ 0 (down)

5. Round the numbers to the nearest thousand.

a. 3,520 ≈ _____   b. 6,709 ≈ _____   c. 5,499 ≈ _____

d. 7,230 ≈ _____   e. 2,800 ≈ _____   f. 4,087 ≈ _____

6. Round these numbers to the nearest thousand.

a. 526 ≈ _____   b. 54 ≈ _____   c. 761 ≈ _____

d. 4,197 ≈ _____   e. 5,672 ≈ _____   f. 3,099 ≈ _____

g. 2,907 ≈ _____   h. 5,502 ≈ _____   i. 9,397 ≈ _____

j. 9,605 ≈ _____   k. 2,553 ≈ _____   l. 1,047 ≈ _____

7. Round these numbers to the nearest ten, nearest hundred, and nearest thousand.

n	55	2,602	9,829	495	709	5,328
rounded to nearest 10						
rounded to nearest 100						
rounded to nearest 1000						

Estimating

To **estimate** the result of a calculation, round the numbers, and then calculate (add, subtract, multiply, or divide) using the rounded numbers. Your result will not be exact, and it will be called an **estimation**.

Use the symbol " $\approx$ " (approximately) instead of using the equals sign " $=$ " when you change from exact numbers to rounded numbers.

For example: $567 + 89 - 413 \approx 600 + 100 - 400 = 300.$

1. First estimate by rounding the numbers to the nearest hundred. Then find the exact answer.

a. Estimate: $967 \quad + \quad 231 \quad + \quad 4{,}792$ $\downarrow \qquad\qquad \downarrow \qquad\qquad \downarrow$ $\approx \quad 1{,}000 \quad + \qquad\qquad + \qquad\qquad = \underline{\hspace{2cm}}$	**Calculate exactly:** $\qquad\quad 9\ \ 6\ \ 7$ $\qquad\quad 2\ \ 3\ \ 1$ $+\ 4\ \ 7\ \ 9\ \ 2$ $\overline{\qquad\qquad\qquad}$
b. Estimate: $320 \quad + \quad 405 \quad + \quad 587$ $\downarrow \qquad\qquad \downarrow \qquad\qquad \downarrow$ $\approx \qquad\quad + \qquad\qquad + \qquad\qquad = \underline{\hspace{2cm}}$	**Calculate exactly:**
c. Estimate: $1{,}029 \quad - \quad 372 \quad - \quad 105$ $\downarrow \qquad\qquad \downarrow \qquad\qquad \downarrow$ $\approx \qquad\quad - \qquad\qquad - \qquad\qquad = \underline{\hspace{2cm}}$	**Calculate exactly:**
d. Estimate: $3{,}492 \quad - \quad 1{,}540 \quad - \quad 211$ $\downarrow \qquad\qquad \downarrow \qquad\qquad \downarrow$ $\approx \qquad\quad - \qquad\qquad - \qquad\qquad = \underline{\hspace{2cm}}$	**Calculate exactly:**

2. Each bus can take 47 passengers. Estimate: *about* how many passengers are in four full buses?

3. The table lists the costs of running a snack bar during recess. Round the numbers to the nearest ten, and then estimate the total cost over these five weeks.

Week 37	Week 38	Week 39	Week 40	Week 41
$147	$164	$182	$129	$131

4. Mary's family is going to rent an apartment for a three-week vacation. They have two choices: one apartment costs $289 per week and another costs $327 per week.

   a. Estimate the cost of each apartment (for 3 weeks).

   Apartment 1: about _____

   Apartment 2: about _____

   b. *Approximately* how much would the family save by choosing the cheaper rental?

5. The bar graph lists the number of loans in the Charleston library in the weeks of May and June. From this graph, you cannot read the exact numbers of loans, but you can find the *approximate* numbers. Estimate, to the nearest ten, the total number of loans for:

   a. weeks 18-21

   b. weeks 22-25

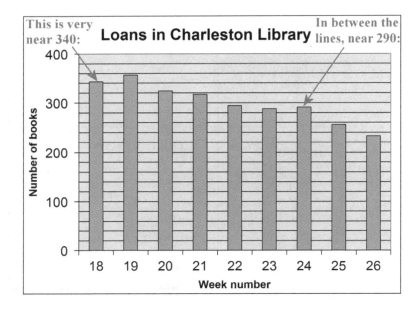

40

Money and Discounts

Remember? Add up to find change.	Price: $3.37. Customer gave $5.
To figure out change, find the <u>difference</u> between the price and the money given. Start from the price and add till you reach the amount the customer gave.	$3.37 $3.40 $4.00 $5.00 differences → 3 ¢ 60 ¢ $1 Change: $1.63

1. Write the dollar amounts as cents or vice versa.

   a. $0.25 = _____ ¢   **b.** $1.78 = _____ ¢   **c.** $15.60 = _____ ¢

   d. $_____ = 20¢   **e.** $_____ = 154¢   **f.** $_____ = 859¢

2. You bought items for $1.50, $12, and for $2.20. You paid with a 20-dollar bill.

   a. How much was your total?

   b. How much was your change?

3. Make change. Mark how many of each bill/coin you need. The first one is done for you.
   Use mental math, like you have learned in the previous grades.

Item cost	Money given	Change needed	$50 bill	$20 bill	$5 bill	$1 bill
a. $56	$70	*$ 1 4*			*2*	*4*
b. $78	$100					
c. $129	$200					

4. Make change. Mark how many of each bill or coin you need.

Item cost	Money given	Change needed	$5 bill	$1 bill	25¢	10¢	5¢	1¢
a. $2.56	$5							
b. $7.08	$10							
c. $3.37	$10							

5. Match the situations (a), (b), and (c) with number sentences (i), (ii), and (iii).
   Then solve for the unknown number x in each situation.

a. Andy had $60 and he bought a tool set for $48. How much does he have left?	**i.** $60 - x = $48 $x = $ _____
b. Elisa bought food for $60 and now has $48 left. How much money did she have initially?	**ii.** $60 - $48 = x $x = $ _____
c. Greg had $60 when he went to the store. He came back home with $48. How much did he spend?	**iii.** $x - $60 = $48 $x = $ _____

6. Solve. Write a number sentence with an unknown (x or ? or another symbol) for each problem.
   Then solve it. The first one is done for you.

a. Mike had $99. He spent _____, and he has $56 left.	$99 - x = $56 $x = $43
b. Dad had _____. He spent $250, and has $170 left.	
c. Greg bought a tool for $45 and now he has $15 left. How much did he have originally?	
d. Alice had $12. She bought an item, and now she has $3.56. How much did the item cost?	
e. Matt bought a game for $12 and a book for $9. Now he has $29 left. How much did Matt have originally?	
f. David has saved $65. He bought two music books for $12 each and one for $7. How much does he have left now?	
g. Emma had $20. She bought two mugs, and now she has $12.40 left. How much did one mug cost?	
h. Jacob had $50. He bought three packs of batteries, and now he has $17 left. How much did one pack of batteries cost?	

Discounts

Often a store lowers the price of an item. That is called *discounting*.

If a shirt costs $10, and then the store puts a new price of $9 on it, the shirt is *discounted* by $1. The discount is how many dollars the price was lowered. This time the discount was $1.

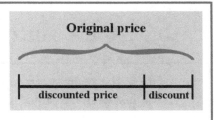

Original price

discounted price | discount

A TV costs $650. Now it is discounted by $100. The new price is $650 − $100 = $550.	A flower vase was discounted by $2.10. The new price is $6. Add to find the original price, which is of course higher: $6 + $2.10 = $8.10

7. A TV set that used to cost $1,199 is discounted by $200.
   What is the new price?

8. What is the discount amount, if a flute that was $178 now costs $159?

9. How much is the discount, the new price, or the original price?

 a. Old price $5.25 New price $4.50 Discount $_____	 **b.** Old price $1.56 New price $1.32 Discount $_____	 **c.** Before $500 / month Now _____ / month Discount $23	 **d.** Before $_____ Now $29.50 Discount $5.50

10. Write an addition or a subtraction with an unknown (*x* or ?). Solve it.

a. A jacket was $54.99; now the price is $47.99. How much was the discount?	⟵ original price $54.99 ⟶ $47.99 | ?

_____

_____

b. The car seat has been discounted by $35, and now it costs $94. What was the original price?	⟵ original price ⟶

_____

_____

Calculate and Estimate Money Amounts

To round to the nearest *ten cents*, look at the <u>one-cents</u> digit (the last digit). Round up or down as usual. • The cent-amount will be in whole tens, so the one-cents digit becomes zero.	$1.4**7** ≈ $1.50 $7.0**2** ≈ $7.00 $6.9**5** ≈ $7.00 $4.8**4** ≈ $4.80
Rounding to the nearest *dollar*, look at the <u>ten-cents</u> digit (tenth of a dollar). Round up or down as usual. • The rounded result is in whole dollars so omit the decimal point and the cents.	$12.**7**2 ≈ $13 $59.**9**2 ≈ $60 $452.**3**4 ≈ $452 $3,480.**5**5 ≈ $3,481
Rounding to the nearest *ten dollars*, look at the <u>dollars</u> digit. Round up or down using the usual rules. • The dollar-amount will be in whole tens, and you can omit the cents and the decimal point.	$4**7**.26 ≈ $50 $56**2**.94 ≈ $560 $3**9**5.60 ≈ $400 $4,53**9**.50 ≈ $4,540

1. Round these numbers to the nearest ten cents.

   a. $6.27 ≈ _____

   b. $9.96 ≈ _____

   c. $5.64 ≈ _____

   d. $0.25 ≈ _____

   e. $0.68 ≈ _____

   f. $5.03 ≈ _____

2. Round these numbers to the nearest dollar.

   a. $3.17 ≈ _____

   b. $97.99 ≈ _____

   c. $3.29 ≈ _____

   d. $1,680.25 ≈ _____

   e. $47.38 ≈ _____

   f. $125.59 ≈ _____

3. Round these numbers to the nearest ten dollars.

   a. $45.70 ≈ _____

   b. $7.99 ≈ _____

   c. $73.78 ≈ _____

   d. $6,289.40 ≈ _____

   e. $43.27 ≈ _____

   f. $169.49 ≈ _____

4. Round these numbers to the nearest ten cents and to the nearest dollar.

n	$29.78	$5.09	$59.95	$2.33	$0.54
rounded to nearest ten cents					
rounded to nearest dollar					

5. Round the prices in problem (a) to the nearest dollar, and in problem (b) to the nearest ten dollars. Then use the rounded prices to estimate the total cost.

   a. Pencils $2.28, paper $5.90, notebook $4.76, books $12.75.

   b. Chairs $124, table $195.99, bed $256, mattresses $342.60.

6. Solve these problems with estimation. You don't need to find the exact answer!

a. A book is $4.87 and another is $6.95. What is the total approximately?	**b.** A gallon of gas is $2.87. About how many gallons can you get with $20?
c. About how much is it to buy five notebooks for $2.08 each and two pencil sets for $4.87 each?	**d.** You have $10. How many ice cream cones can you buy that cost $1.97 each?

Regrouping works the same way with money amounts.	Next, regroup one of the dollars as 10 ten-cents.	Lastly, regroup one of the ten-cents as ten cents, and subtract.
4 10 $ ~~5~~ ~~0~~ . 0 0 − 3 4 . 3 5	9 4 ~~10~~ 10 $ ~~5~~ ~~0~~ . ~~0~~ 0 − 3 4 . 3 5	9 9 4 ~~10~~ ~~10~~ 10 $ ~~5~~ ~~0~~ . ~~0~~ ~~0~~ − 3 4 . 3 5 —————— $ 1 5 . 6 5

7. Subtract with money amounts. Check by adding!

a.	b.
$ 8 0 . 0 0 − 5 6 . 7 0 +	$ 6 0 0 . 0 0 − 2 3 0 . 5 0 +
c.	**d.**
$ 4 0 0 . 0 0 − 1 9 8 . 9 9 +	$ 1 0 9 . 4 0 − 7 8 . 6 5 +

8. The chart lists some ticket prices
   for an amusement park. There are
   varying prices for tickets for adults
   and children. For some tickets,
   there is both a regular price and
   a discounted price.

   Look at the regular prices:
   a. How much more does a 1-day
      ticket cost for an adult than
      a 1-day ticket for a child?

   b. How much more does a 2-day
      ticket cost for an adult than
      a 2-day ticket for a child?

Ticket type	Regular price	Discount price
1-Day Adult	$89	-
1-Day Child	$83	-
2-day Adult	$176	-
2-day Child	$164	-
3-day Adult	$242	$240.38
3-day Child	$226	$224.41
4-day Adult	$256	$253.52
4-day Child	$239	$235.68

   c. Now, compare the regular *and* discounted prices for
      a 4-day ticket for an adult. How much is the discount?

   d. Compare the regular *and* discounted prices for a
      4-day ticket for a child. How much is the discount?

9. A family of two adults and two children is planning to visit the amusement park.

   a. If they plan to spend three days there using the discounted
      tickets, how much would the tickets cost for the entire family?

   b. If they can afford $1,000 at most,
      can they spend four days there?
      Hint: Use rounded numbers and estimate.

Review Chapter 1

1. Subtract or add in your head.

a. $81 - 72 =$ _____	**b.** $45 + 65 =$ _____	**c.** $160 + 280 =$ _____
$665 - 99 =$ _____	$196 + 99 =$ _____	$54 - 28 =$ _____

2. Write a number sentence using x for the problem, and fill in the numbers in the bar model. Then solve. Do *not* just write the answer.

   Mary had saved \$230. Then she bought a flute and some music books. Now she has \$38 left. What is the total cost of her purchases?

   _____

   $x =$ _____

3. Solve $x + 587 = 1{,}394$.

4. Calculate in the right order.

a. $5 \times (2 + 4)$	**b.** $120 - 20 - 2 \times 0$	**c.** $(80 - 44) + (80 - 34)$
$(50 - 20) \times 2 + 10$	$5 \times 3 + 2 \times 7$	$10 \times (4 + 4) - 4$

5. Which number sentence matches the problem below?

   What is the total cost of three hammers at \$13 each when they are discounted by \$2 each?

   $3 \times \$13 - \$2$

   $\$13 - 3 \times \$2$

   $(\$13 - \$2) \times 3$

6. How many feet do ten dogs and 20 chickens have in total? Write a single number sentence to solve this.

7. Estimate the total cost of the items below using rounded numbers. Don't find the exact cost.

Colored pencils $24.85; number cards $13.95; dice $3.31

8. After spending $15.20 on food and $34.60 on gasoline,
   Mom had $70.20 left in her purse.
   How much did she have originally?

9. Alberto bought two pairs of skis. One pair cost
   $48.90 and the other cost $25 more than the first.
   What was the total cost?

Chapter 2: Large Numbers and Place Value
Introduction

The second chapter of *Math Mammoth Grade 4* covers large numbers (up to 1 million) and place value.

The first lessons only deal with thousands, or numbers with a maximum of four digits. These are for review and for deepening the student's understanding of place value, as understanding place value with four-digit numbers is crucial before moving on to larger numbers. After that we go on to numbers with five and six digits (numbers till one million). Students write them in expanded form, compare them, add and subtract them, and learn more about rounding.

Lastly, we briefly study the multiples of 10, 100, and 1000. This lesson prepares the way for some very important ideas in the next chapter (multi-digit multiplication).

Please recall that it is not recommended to assign all the exercises by default. Use your judgment, and strive to vary the number of assigned exercises according to the student's needs.

Helpful Resources on the Internet

You can also access this list of links at **https://l.mathmammoth.com/gr4ch2**

SCAN ME

Can You Say Really Big Numbers?
Enter a really big number, try to say it out loud, and see it written.
https://www.mathcats.com/explore/reallybignumbers.html

Base Ten Blocks
Click on buttons to make blocks appear. The level of difficulty can be adjusted.
https://www.hoodamath.com/mobile/games/basetenblocks.html

Place Value Puzzler
Place value game. Click on the asked place value in a number, or type in the rounded version of the number.
https://www.funbrain.com/games/place-value

Place Value Payoff
Match numbers written in standard form with numbers written in expanded form in this game.
https://www.quia.com/mc/279741.html

Identify Value of a Digit
Test your knowledge of place value with this interactive multiple-choice quiz.
https://www.khanacademy.org/math/cc-fourth-grade-math/imp-place-value-and-rounding-2/imp-intro-to-place-value/e/place_value?modal=1

Sea Life Comparing Numbers
Answer the problems correctly, and add plants, beautiful fish, corals, and more to the sea floor. Choose the number range "5 digit numbers (up to 99.000)".
https://www.free-training-tutorial.com/comparing-numbers/sealife/sl-comparing.html

Order Numbers - Online Practice
Practice placing numbers in order with this interactive activity.
https://www.mathmammoth.com/practice/order-numbers#questions=10&digits=5&baskets=4

Online Addition Practice
Practice adding large numbers in expanded form with this interactive online exercise.
https://www.mathmammoth.com/practice/place-value#mode=write-number&max-digits=6&question-number=10

Missing Addend Addition Practice
Find the missing number in each addition problem in this interactive online exercise.
https://www.mathmammoth.com/practice/place-value#mode=missing-part&max-digits=6&question-number=10

Addition Quiz
Practice adding in columns in this 10-question online quiz.
https://www.thatquiz.org/tq-1/?-jg41-l34-p0

Place Value Worksheets, Riddles, and Challenges
This page offers a variety of printable activities that practice place value on a fourth grade level.
https://www.math-salamanders.com/4th-grade-place-value.html

Complements of 1,000 Interactive Mad Maths
Answer as many questions as you can in this interactive timed addition quiz.
http://www.snappymaths.com/addition/make1000/interactive/make1000imin/make1000imin.htm

Adding and Subtracting Powers of Ten
Practice adding and subtracting powers of ten up to 1,000,000 in this interactive online quiz.
http://www.snappymaths.com/addsub/addsubp10/interactive/addsubpowers10/addsubpowers10.htm

Money Word Problems Worksheets: Addition and Subtraction
Practice addition and subtraction of various amounts of money with these printable worksheets.
https://www.dadsworksheets.com/worksheets/money-word-problems-addition-and-subtraction.html

ROUNDING AND ESTIMATING

Online Rounding Practice
Reinforce your rounding skills with this interactive online exercise
https://www.mathmammoth.com/practice/rounding#number-range=0to1000000&round-to=any-place

Rounding Sharks
Round numbers to the nearest hundred. Click on the shark that has the correctly rounded number.
https://www.free-training-tutorial.com/rounding/sharks.html

Rounding Quiz
Practice rounding large numbers with this interactive 10-question quiz.
https://www.thatquiz.org/tq-c/?-jg020-l5-mpnv600-p0

Rounding to Thousands, Ten Thousands, or Hundred Thousands (Tutorialspoint.com)
Practice your rounding skills with this online multiple-choice quiz.
https://bit.ly/round-ten-thousand

Thousands

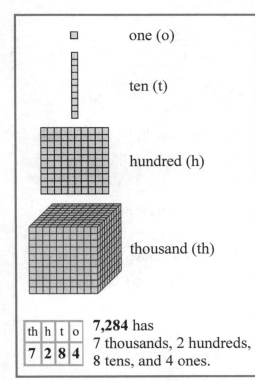

one (o)

ten (t)

hundred (h)

thousand (th)

th	h	t	o
7	2	8	4

7,284 has
7 thousands, 2 hundreds,
8 tens, and 4 ones.

Look at the pictures. How many...
- ones go into a ten? _____
- tens go into a hundred? _____
- hundreds go into a thousand? _____

The way we write numbers is based on number *ten*.

Writing the number 5,608 in **expanded form** means we write out the number <u>as a sum</u> of whole thousands, whole hundreds, whole tens, and ones. You can see all of this right from the number:

- It has <u>5</u> thousands = 5,000
- It has <u>6</u> hundreds = 600
- It has <u>0</u> tens = 0
- It has <u>8</u> ones = 8

Now write it as a sum: 5,608 = 5,000 + 600 + 0 + 8

1. Write the numbers in expanded form.

   a. 8,325 = 8000 + 300 + 20 + 5   **b.** 4,935 =

   c. 4,039 =   **d.** 3,002 =

   e. 2,090 =   **f.** 9,405 =

2. Write the numbers in normal form.

   a. 4000 + 500 + 90 + 3   **b.** 2000 + 90

   c. 3000 + 200   **d.** 8000 + 5

   e. 4 thousand, 6 hundred   **f.** 8 tens, 4 thousand

   g. 3 ones, 7 thousand, 2 hundred   **h.** 4 hundred, 5 ones, 1 thousand

   i. fifty, 7 thousand   **j.** 4 thousand, 5 ones

   k. 9 ones, sixty, 4 thousand   **l.** 8 hundred, 3 thousand, 9 ones

The 7, 2, 8, and 4 are called **digits** of the number 7,284, but 7 in the number 7,284 actually means seven thousand. The **value** of the digit 7 is 7,000.
The 2 in the number 7,284 actually means two hundred. The *value* of the digit 2 is 200.
The *value* of the digit 8 is eighty or 80. The value of the digit 4 is four.

The value of any digit in a number depends on its **place** (where it is located).

6<u>9</u>0	"9" in 690 means ninety.	The value of the digit "9" is 90.	"9" is in the tens place.
<u>9</u>,055	"9" in 9,055 means nine thousand.	The value of the digit "9" is 9,000.	"9" is in the thousands place.
41<u>9</u>	"9" in 419 means just nine.	The value of the digit "9" is 9.	"9" is in the ones place.
1,<u>9</u>70	"9" in 1,970 means nine hundred.	The value of the digit "9" is 900.	"9" is in the hundreds place.

We write numbers using a **place-value notation:** each digit has a place and a value.

Examples. If nine is in the hundreds place, then its value is 900 (such as in the number 5,900). If nine is in the tens place, then its value is 90 (such as in the number 498).

3. What is the value of the digit 5 in the following numbers?

   a. 3,8<u>5</u>9 *fifty*   **b.** 2,506

   c. 5,012   **d.** 3,050

4. Write or tell the value of the underlined digit.

   a. <u>5</u>09 *five hundred*   **b.** <u>9</u>,843

   c. 9<u>4</u>0   **d.** 2,0<u>8</u>8

   e. 1,<u>2</u>00   **f.** 4,00<u>2</u>

   g. 7,9<u>2</u>8   **h.** 74<u>5</u>

5. **a.** What is the largest possible number you can build with the digits 2, 5, 8, and 4?

   b. What is the smallest possible number you can build with them?

6. What is the *difference* between the largest and the smallest possible numbers you can build with the digits 6, 9, and 1?

What is 4,769 + 10?	4,769 has 6 tens. One ten more means there will be 7 tens: 4,779.	

What is 2,958 + 100? 2,958 has nine hundreds. One hundred more means there will be 10 hundreds, but that makes a thousand. Our answer will have 3 thousands and no hundreds: 3,058.

7. Fill in the table, adding 10, 100, or 1,000. If in doubt, you can add in columns.

n	2,508	342	4,009	59	6,980	8,299
$n + 10$						
$n + 100$						
$n + 1000$						

8. What is missing?

    a. $4{,}036 = 4{,}000 + \underline{\hspace{1.5cm}} + 30$ **b.** $483 = 80 + 3 + \underline{\hspace{1.5cm}}$

    c. $9{,}328 = 300 + 9{,}000 + \underline{\hspace{1cm}} + 20$ **d.** $8{,}005 = 5 + \underline{\hspace{1.5cm}}$

    e. $5{,}320 = 20 + \underline{\hspace{1.5cm}} + 300$ **f.** $7{,}609 = 9 + \underline{\hspace{1.5cm}} + 7{,}000$

9. If you add 1 thousand, 1 hundred, 1 ten, and 1 to this number, it becomes 9,000. What is the number?

Puzzle Corner	Build the largest and the least possible number you can with the given digits. Then find their difference (subtract).

a. 7 and 5	**b.** 2 and 9	**c.** 4 and 5	**d.** 8 and 3
75 and 57 *difference: 18*			

e. In which multiplication table can you find each of the differences?

f. Find two (single) digits so that when you do the same thing you did above, the difference is 36.

g. Find two digits so that when you do the same thing you did above, the difference is 27.

h. Find two digits so that when you do the same thing you did above, the difference is 81.

At the Edge of Whole Thousands

Just *one* is missing from a thousand: 999 + 1 = 1,000	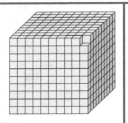
Ten is missing from a thousand: 990 + 10 = 1,000	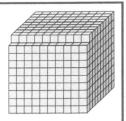

1. How much is missing from a thousand? Write an addition sentence.

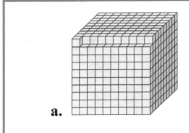

a.

_____ + _____ = 1,000

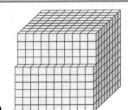

b.

_____ + _____ = 1,000

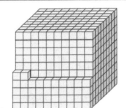

c.

_____ + _____ = 1,000

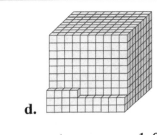

d.

_____ + _____ = 1,000

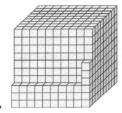

e.

_____ + _____ = 1,000

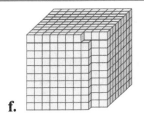

f.

_____ + _____ = 1,000

2. We have 900-something. Complete a thousand.

a. 999 + _1_ = _1,000_	**b.** 980 + _____ = _____	**c.** 930 + _____ = _____
992 + ___ = _____	985 + _____ = _____	937 + _____ = _____

3. Complete the *next* whole thousand.

a.	b.	c.
1,920 + _____ = _____	1,990 + _____ = _____	6,950 + _____ = _____
1,999 + _____ = _____	7,940 + _____ = _____	4,900 + _____ = _____
2,998 + _____ = _____	5,970 + _____ = _____	3,995 + _____ = _____

4. Subtract from whole thousands.

a. $2{,}000 - 1 =$ _____	**b.** $5{,}000 - 3 =$ _____	**c.** $6{,}000 - 50 =$ _____
$2{,}000 - 4 =$ _____	$4{,}000 - 10 =$ _____	$9{,}000 - 30 =$ _____
$2{,}000 - 7 =$ _____	$7{,}000 - 20 =$ _____	$10{,}000 - 100 =$ _____

Mental math trick: Add up to find the difference to the next whole thousand.
First fill the next whole ten, then the next whole hundred, and lastly the next thousand.

$$+\;8 \qquad +\;10 \qquad +\;200$$
$$6{,}782 \quad 6{,}790 \qquad 6{,}800 \quad 7{,}000$$
So, $6{,}782 + 218 = 7{,}000$.

$$+\;50 \qquad +\;200$$
$$5{,}750 \quad 5{,}800 \qquad 6{,}000$$
So, $5{,}750 + 250 = 6{,}000$.

5. Round the numbers to the nearest thousand, and write the **rounding error:** the difference between the number and the rounded number.

Number	Rounded number	Rounding error	Number	Rounded number	Rounding error
4,993			8,029		
7,890			5,113		
9,880			2,810		

6. Solve. Use the top problem to help you solve the ones in the middle and bottom.

a. $2{,}000 - 100 =$ _____	**b.** $5{,}000 - 200 =$ _____	**c.** $9{,}000 - 500 =$ _____
$2{,}000 - 150 =$ _____	$5{,}000 - 230 =$ _____	$9{,}000 - 580 =$ _____
$2{,}000 - 250 =$ _____	$5{,}000 - 280 =$ _____	$9{,}000 - 680 =$ _____

7. Mark bought a computer for $1,997 and a monitor for $995.

   a. Estimate the total cost in whole thousand dollars.

   b. How many dollars short of that estimate is the exact cost?

8. What is the rounding error, if the sum $1{,}982 + 3{,}950$ is rounded to $6{,}000$?

More Thousands

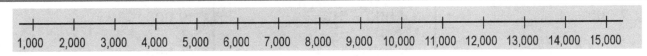

1,000 2,000 3,000 4,000 5,000 6,000 7,000 8,000 9,000 10,000 11,000 12,000 13,000 14,000 15,000

On this number line we see whole thousands marked from one thousand to fifteen thousand.

In the numbers on the right, the colored digits tell us the number of whole thousands. A comma separates those digits from the rest of the number.

Read the colored digits as a number by itself, and when you come to the comma, say the word "thousand."

We continue with whole thousands until we reach *a thousand* thousands. That number has a new name: **one million**.

7 8,0 0 0	*Read:* 78 thousand
1 5 3,0 0 0	*Read:* 153 thousand
8 0 2,0 0 0	*Read:* 802 thousand
9 9 0,0 0 0	*Read:* 990 thousand
9 9 9,0 0 0	*Read:* 999 thousand
1,0 0 0,0 0 0	Thousand thousand = 1 million

The rest of the digits (not colored) tell us the hundreds, tens, and ones just like you have learned in the past.

1 7,5 4 4	*Read:* 17 thousand five hundred forty four
6 0 9,2 3 0	*Read:* 609 thousand two hundred thirty
7 0,0 8 0	*Read:* 70 thousand eighty
9 0 2,0 0 5	*Read:* 902 thousand five

1. Place a comma in the number to separate the thousands. Fill in the missing parts.

a. 1 6 4 0 0 0	b. 9 2 0 0 0	c. 3 0 9 0 0 0	d. 3 4 0 0 0	e. 7 8 0 0 0 0
_____ thousand	_____ thousand	_____ thousand	_____ thousand	_____ thousand

2. Place a comma in the number. Fill in missing parts. Read the numbers aloud.

a. 1 6 4,4 5 3	b. 9 2 9 0 8	c. 3 2 9 0 3 3	d. 1 4 0 0 4
164 thousand *453*	_____ thousand _____	_____ thousand _____	_____ thousand _____
e. 5 5 0 0 5 3	f. 7 2 0 0 1	g. 8 0 0 0 0 4	h. 3 0 0 3 6
_____ thousand _____	_____ thousand _____	_____ thousand _____	_____ thousand _____

3. Read these numbers aloud.

a. 456,098   b. 950,050   c. 23,090   d. 560,008

e. 78,304   f. 266,894   g. 1,000,000   h. 306,700

4. Think in whole thousands and add!

a. $30,000 + 5,000 =$
think: 30 thousand + 5 thousand

b. $200,000 + 1,000 =$

c. $400,000 + 30,000 =$

d. $710,000 + 40,000 =$

e. $300,000 + 700,000 =$

f. $700,000 + 70,000 =$

5. Add and subtract, thinking in whole thousands.

a. $35,000 + 5,000 =$

b. $711,000 + 10,000 =$

c. $420,000 + 30,000 =$

d. $700,000 - 70,000 =$

e. $300,000 - 60,000 =$

f. $1,000,000 - 200,000 =$

g. $30,000 - 5,000 =$

h. $200,000 - 6,000 =$

i. $723,000 - 400,000 =$

j. $500,000 - 1,000 =$

6. The numbers 510,000 and 520,000 are marked on the number line below (at the "posts").
   Write the numbers that correspond to the dots.

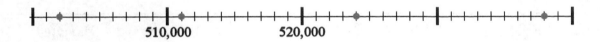

510,000   520,000

7. Make a number line from 320,000 to 340,000 with tick-marks at every whole thousand, similar
   to the one above. Then mark the following numbers on the number line:
   323,000 328,000 335,000 329,000 330,000

57

Practicing with Thousands

35 thousand 4 3 5 , 0 0 4	There are no hundreds or tens. So, we put a zero in the hundreds place and in the tens place.	203 thousand sixty 2 0 3 , 0 6 0	There are no hundreds or ones. So, we put a zero in the hundreds place and in the ones place.

1. Break these numbers into whole thousands, hundreds, tens, and ones.

a. 49,015	**b.** 206,090
_4 9_ thousands ____hundreds ____ tens ____ ones	____ thousands ____hundreds _____ tens _____ ones
c. 107,802	**d.** 88,030
____ thousands ____hundreds _____ tens _____ ones	____ thousands ____hundreds _____ tens _____ ones
e. 790,302	**f.** 903,000
____ thousands ____hundreds _____ tens _____ ones	____ thousands ____hundreds _____ tens _____ ones
g. 250,067	**h.** 300,070
____ thousands ____hundreds _____ tens _____ ones	____ thousands ____hundreds _____ tens _____ ones

2. Write the numbers.

a. 20 thousand 7 hundreds 4 ones	**b.** 204 thousand 8 tens	**c.** 101 thousand 6 hundred
d. 540 thousand 4 ones	**e.** 230 thousand 3 hundred 7 tens	**f.** 9 thousand 6 hundred 7 ones
g. 873 thousand 5 tens	**h.** 40 thousand 4 hundred	**i.** 59 thousand 6 tens 5 ones

3. Write the numbers. The parts are in scrambled order.

a. 4 tens 25 thousand 7 ones 3 hundred	**b.** 2 tens 700 thousand 6 hundred 4 ones	**c.** 8 hundred 1 thousand 60 thousand 8 ones
d. 50 thousand 6 tens 3 thousand	**e.** 42 thousand 7 ones 8 tens	**f.** 1000 thousand
g. 90 thousand 4 tens 200 thousand	**h.** 20 thousand 9 hundred 7 thousand 5 ones	**i.** 500 thousand 4 thousand 8 ones

4. Continue the patterns.

a.	b.	c.	d.
45,000	134,000	800,000	400,000
45,500	134,200	750,000	390,000
46,000	134,400	700,000	380,000
49,000	135,600	400,000	320,000

5. Add.

a. $30{,}000 + 50 =$

b. $254{,}000 + 300 + 5 =$

c. $133{,}000 + 200 + 50 =$

d. $77{,}000 + 4 =$

e. $2 + 60{,}000 =$

f. $120{,}000 + 3 + 60 =$

g. $5{,}000 + 10{,}000 + 20 =$

h. $4{,}000 + 6 + 20{,}000 =$

i. $300 + 30{,}000 + 90 =$

j. $400 + 86{,}000 + 70 + 1 =$

Place Value with Thousands

728 thousand 451

hth	tth	th	h	t	o
7	2	8,	4	5	1

Each of the six digits has its own place ("box" in the picture).

Each of the "places" has its own value.

In the charts:

"hth" means hundred thousands
"tth" means ten thousands
"th" means thousands

- "7" is in the **hundred thousands** place. The value of "7" is seven hundred thousand.

- "2" is in the **ten thousands** place. The value of "2" is twenty thousand.

- "8" is in the **thousands** place. The value of "8" is eight thousand.

- "4" is in the hundreds place. The value of "4" is four hundred.

- "5" is in the tens place. The value of "5" is fifty.

- "1" is in the ones place. The value of "1" is one.

728 thousand 451

hth	tth	th	h	t	o
7	2	8,	4	5	1
7	0	0,	0	0	0
	2	0,	0	0	0
		8,	0	0	0
			4	0	0
				5	0
					1

728,451 written in expanded form is
700,000 + 20,000 + 8,000 + 400 + 50 + 1

501,029 written in expanded form is
500,000 + 1,000 + 20 + 9

501 thousand 029

hth	tth	th	h	t	o
5	0	1,	0	2	9
5	0	0,	0	0	0
		1,	0	0	0
				2	0
					9

1. Fill in the place value charts.

a.

hth	tth	th	h	t	o
	8	7,	0	1	5

b.

hth	tth	th	h	t	o
4	0	3,	2	8	0

c.

hth	tth	th	h	t	o
6	9	2,	0	0	4

d.

hth	tth	th	h	t	o
7	0	0,	2	0	4

2. Write the numbers from exercise (1a) and (1b) in expanded form.

   a.

   b.

3. Write the numbers in expanded form.

   a. 32,493

   b. 172,392

   c. 25,600

   d. 109,020

   e. 900,701

4. Find the missing numbers.

   a. $20{,}290 = 90 + \underline{\hspace{2cm}} + 200$ **b.** $205{,}500 = 200{,}000 + 500 + \underline{\hspace{2cm}}$

   c. $80{,}020 = 80{,}000 + \underline{\hspace{1.5cm}}$ **d.** $707{,}070 = 70 + 700{,}000 + \underline{\hspace{2cm}}$

   e. $778{,}090 = 90 + 8{,}000 + \underline{\hspace{1.5cm}} + 700{,}000$

5. What is the value of the digit 5 in the following numbers?

   a. **5**13,829 *five hundred thousand*   **b.** 400,06**5**

   c. 700,**5**49   **d.** **5**9,906

6. Write the value of the underlined digit in words.

   a. **18**,209   **b.** **3**00,094

   c. **8**9,605   **d.** 20**8**,000

   e. 302,**6**00   **f.** 300,0**27**

   g. 2**1**0,408   **h.** **9**21,993

7. What are these numbers?

   a. 8 is in tens place, 5 is in hundred thousands place, and 7 is in ones place.

   b. 4 is in hundreds place, 8 is in tens place, and 2 is in ten thousands place.

   c. 7 is in thousands place, 9 is in hundred thousands place, and 7 is in hundreds place.

   d. 6 is in tens place, 5 is in ten thousands place, and 3 is in hundreds place.

Puzzle Corner	My hundred thousands digit is double my ten thousands digit, and my ten thousands digit is triple my ones digit. The rest—zeros. Who am I?

Comparing with Thousands

Example. Which is more, 399,393 or 393,939?

You are used to comparing small numbers. When comparing large numbers, use the same principles:

- Check if one number contains bigger units (or is "longer"). For example, 675,000 > 95,239 because 95,239 does not have any hundred thousands, but 675,000 does.

- If the numbers have the same amount of digits (are equally "long"), then you need to compare the digits in the different places, starting at the largest place value unit. Place value charts can help.

hth	tth	th	h	t	o
3	9	9	3	9	3
3	9	3	9	3	9

↑ start comparing at the largest place value (hundred thousands)

- Start at the hundred thousands place. The digits are the same (3). Both numbers have 300,000.

- At the ten thousands place, the digits are the same. Both numbers have 90,000.

- At the thousands place, one number has 9, the other has 3. The upper number has 9,000 while the other has only 3,000!

Therefore 399,393 > 393,939

tth	th	h	t	o
2	7	0	4	5
2	7	0	5	4

↑ start comparing here.

- Start at the ten thousands place. The digits are the same (2). Both numbers have 20,000.

- At the thousands place, the digits are the same. Both numbers have 7,000.

- At the hundreds place, the digits are the same.

- At the tens place, one number has 4, the other has 5.

Therefore 27,045 < 27,054

1. Write < or > between the numbers. These are fairly easy!

a. 45,200 54,000	**b.** 18,700 191,000	**c.** 22,029 202,000
d. 78,111 77,001	**e.** 5,605 605,000	**f.** 34,092 43,200
g. 1,788 17,880	**h.** 392,000 365,000	**i.** 493,239 521,000

2. Write the numbers in order from smallest to greatest.

a. 18,309; 81,390; 8,039; 818,039

b. 52,000; 5,020; 250,000; 520,000

3. Find the largest number.

a.	b.	c.
45,500 54,000 52,400	7,887 8,708 7,708	10,101 11,001 11,101
d.	**e.**	**f.**
134,000 144,000 143,400	5,606 5,556 5,599	8,099 8,909 8,009

4. Write < or > between the numbers. Use the place value charts if you need to.

a. 78,187 77,817	b. 21,089 21,098
c. 23,392 23,293	d. 349,309 343,909
e. 493,605 465,093	f. 199,909 20,900
g. 545,055 545,405	h. 909,808 908,809

hth	tth	th	h	t	o

hth	tth	th	h	t	o

hth	tth	th	h	t	o

hth	tth	th	h	t	o

hth	tth	th	h	t	o

5. Look at the number lines and mark the following numbers (approximately) there with little dots.

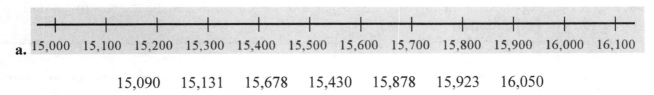

a. 15,000 15,100 15,200 15,300 15,400 15,500 15,600 15,700 15,800 15,900 16,000 16,100

15,090   15,131   15,678   15,430   15,878   15,923   16,050

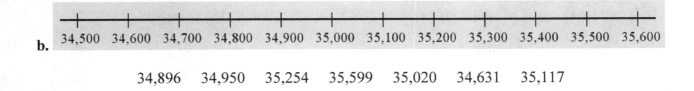

b. 34,500 34,600 34,700 34,800 34,900 35,000 35,100 35,200 35,300 35,400 35,500 35,600

34,896   34,950   35,254   35,599   35,020   34,631   35,117

6. Write the numbers in order on the lines below.

67,250   67,030   67,510   67,780   67,940   67,370   67,049   67,703

_____ < _____ < _____ < _____ <

_____ < _____ < _____ < _____

7. Find the largest number. It helps to write the comma that separates the thousands in the numbers.

a.	b.	c.
383800 39903 398039	290290 92022 99029	600606 606660 606066
d.	**e.**	**f.**
49830 93024 110293	3420 301481 30420	379444 390200 390002

8. Write the numbers in order.

a. 500   5,600   5,505   5,406   1,500 1,459

_____ < _____ < _____ < _____ < _____ < _____

b. 87,600   8,708   78,777   78,707 77,988 7,800

_____ < _____ < _____ < _____ < _____ < _____

9. Find the number that fits in place of x.

a. $500{,}000 - x = 300{,}000$	**b.** $x + 30{,}000 = 100{,}000$	**c.** $x + x = 10{,}000$
$x =$ _____	$x =$ _____	$x =$ _____

10. **a.** Figure out the pattern in the top row. Then, add 500 to each number in the top row to get the numbers in the bottom row.

n	600	1,200	1,800	2,400			
$n + 500$	*1100*						

   b. If you look only at the numbers in the bottom row, what pattern do you see?

   Can you explain why that is?

11. **a.** Add 3,000 each time to get the numbers in the top row. Then, subtract 5,000 from each number in the top row to get the numbers in the bottom row.

n	52,000	55,000	58,000			
$n - 5{,}000$	*47,000*					

   b. If you look only at the numbers in the bottom row, what pattern do you see?

Adding and Subtracting Big Numbers

1. Add large numbers exactly the same way as you add smaller numbers. See how well you can do!

a. $\begin{array}{r} 905,091 \\ + \quad 40,510 \\ \hline \end{array}$	**b.** $\begin{array}{r} 29,313 \\ + \; 407,616 \\ \hline \end{array}$	**c.** $\begin{array}{r} 289,300 \\ 120,000 \\ + \; 409,436 \\ \hline \end{array}$
d. $\begin{array}{r} 89,502 \\ 45,987 \\ + \; 13,770 \\ \hline \end{array}$	**e.** $\begin{array}{r} 560,421 \\ 340,060 \\ + \quad 4,987 \\ \hline \end{array}$	**f.** $\begin{array}{r} 299,674 \\ 178,498 \\ + \quad 45,988 \\ \hline \end{array}$

2. Continue the patterns. Use mental math.

a.	b.	c.
29,100	906,500	610,400
29,300	916,600	610,000
29,500	926,700	609,600
30,900	997,400	606,800

Subtraction happens the same way as with smaller numbers. Just be careful with regrouping!	7 10 $\cancel{8}\cancel{0}0,000$ $-\ 510,065$ _____ Regroup...	9 7 $\cancel{10}$ 10 $\cancel{8}\cancel{0}0,000$ $-\ 510,065$ _____ Keep regrouping...	9 9 7 $\cancel{10}$ $\cancel{10}$ 10 $\cancel{8}\cancel{0}0,\cancel{0}00$ $-\ 513,065$ _____ (Complete the problem.)

3. Subtract.

a. $\quad 120,091$ $-\ \ \ 34,510$ _____	**b.** $\quad 199,136$ $-\ \ \ 79,160$ _____	**c.** $\quad 670,000$ $-\ \ \ \ \ 1,300$ _____
d. $\quad 234,688$ $-\ 167,991$ _____	**e.** $\quad 65,570$ $-\ 23,677$ _____	**f.** $\quad 90,080$ $-\ \ 5,025$ _____
g. $\quad 554,600$ $-\ 128,000$ _____	**h.** $\quad 600,000$ $-223,065$ _____	**i.** $\quad 400,000$ $-\ 18,344$ _____

4. Match the calculations that have the same answer.

a.			**b.**	
$419,000 + 1,000$	$150,000 + 40,000$		$500,000 - 3,000$	$140,000 + 70,000$
$500 + 36,000$	$20,000 + 400,000$		$189,000 - 80,000$	$97,000 + 400,000$
$189,000 + 1,000$	$36,100 + 400$		$40,600 - 500$	$20,000 + 20,100$
$40,500 + 500$	$180,000 - 2,000$		$250,000 - 40,000$	$100,000 + 9,000$
$177,300 + 700$	$36,000 + 5,000$		$77,700 - 7,000$	$100,000 - 29,300$

Line up the ones, tens, hundreds, thousands, and so on - even the commas!			
``` 134,607 + 3,065 ```	``` 134,607 + 3,065 ```	``` 457,934 37,921 + 24 ```	``` 457,934 37,921 + 24 ```
NOT THIS WAY! (numbers not lined up)	This is good! Complete the problem.	**THIS IS OFF!** (numbers not lined up)	This is good! Complete the problem.

5. Calculate. Line up all the place value units carefully.

      a. $300{,}145 + 2{,}399 + 345$ **b.** $560{,}073 + 81{,}400 + 98$

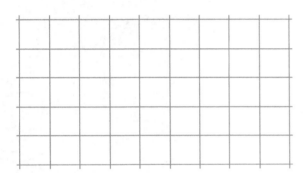 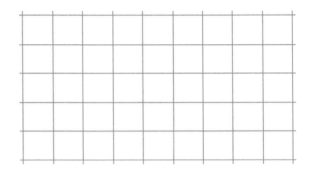

      c. $23{,}000 + 456 + 3{,}256$ **d.** $345 + 870{,}077 + 32 + 5{,}801$

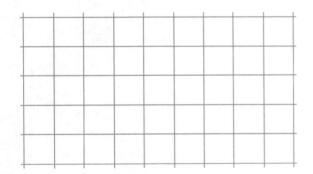 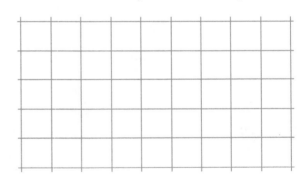

6. Add a thousand, a ten thousand, or a hundred thousand to the given numbers.

n	13,000	78,000	154,000	500,000	640,500
$n + 1{,}000$					
$n + 10{,}000$					
$n + 100{,}000$					

Line up the ones, tens, hundreds, and so on - even the commas.			
5 0 9 , 0 3 2 – 2 1 9	5 0 9 , 0 3 2 – 2 1 9	2 4 5 , 0 3 2 – 3 7 , 9 2 1 1 1 8 , 1 1 1	2 4 5 , 0 3 2 – 3 7 , 9 2 1
NOT THIS WAY! (numbers not lined up)	This is correct! Complete the problem.	**THIS IS WRONG** (errors in regrouping)	You do the problem correctly!

7. Calculate.

     a. 509,788 – 82,345   **b.** 30,760 – 2,906

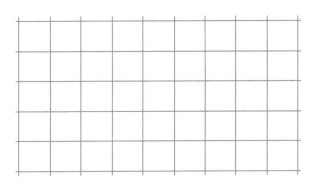 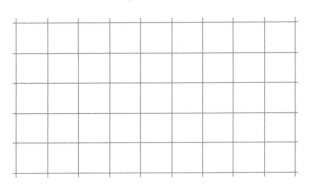

     c. 26,509 – 1,208   **d.** 984,044 – 329

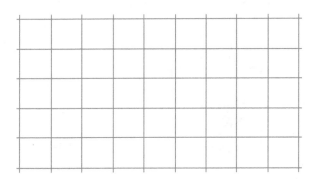 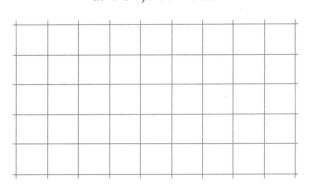

8. Compare the two expressions (calculations) and write < , > or = .

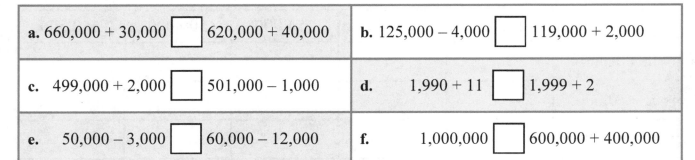

a. 660,000 + 30,000 ☐ 620,000 + 40,000		**b.** 125,000 – 4,000 ☐ 119,000 + 2,000	
c. 499,000 + 2,000 ☐ 501,000 – 1,000		**d.** 1,990 + 11 ☐ 1,999 + 2	
e. 50,000 – 3,000 ☐ 60,000 – 12,000		**f.** 1,000,000 ☐ 600,000 + 400,000	

Rounding and Estimating with Large Numbers

We can round numbers to the nearest ten, to the nearest hundred, to the nearest thousand, to the nearest ten thousand, and so on—to *any* place. No matter what place we are rounding to, the *rules of rounding* are the same.

Rules of rounding whole numbers

Look at the digit AFTER the place you are rounding to:

- If that digit is 0, 1, 2, 3, or 4, then round DOWN.

- If that digit is 5, 6, 7, 8, or 9, then round UP.

- Change to zeros all the digits *after* the place you are rounding to.

- If rounding up, the digit in the place you are rounding to is increased by 1.

Remember, the squiggly equals sign (" ≈ ") is read "is about," or "is approximately."

To help us, let's draw a line ┊ between the digit we are rounding to and the next smaller one.

Rounding to the nearest TEN:	Rounding to the nearest HUNDRED:	Rounding to the nearest THOUSAND:
2,56┊7 ≈ 2,57┊0	2,5┊67 ≈ 2,6┊00	23,┊802 ≈ 24,┊000
395,84┊9 ≈ 395,85┊0	395,8┊49 ≈ 395,8┊00	980,┊097 ≈ 980,┊000

Rounding to the nearest TEN THOUSAND:	Rounding to the nearest HUNDRED THOUSAND:	
72┊6,451 ≈ 73┊0,000	8┊67,300 ≈ 9┊00,000	
95┊3,987 ≈ 95┊0,000	1┊26,835 ≈ 1┊00,000	

1. Round the numbers as the dashed line indicates (to the underlined digit).

a. 45┊2,550 ≈	**b.** 86┊,256 ≈	**c.** 77,5┊79 ≈
d. 245,┊250 ≈	**e.** 8┊94,077 ≈	**f.** 385,┊706 ≈
g. 6┊15,493 ≈	**h.** 5┊27,009 ≈	**i.** 2┊52,000 ≈
j. 2┊6,566 ≈	**k.** 94┊4,032 ≈	**l.** 335,┊700 ≈
m. 48,42┊1 ≈	**n.** 8,5┊55 ≈	**o.** 40┊9,239 ≈

A note about the digit 9

If you are rounding up, and the digit that you need to increase by one is a 9, you have to make it a 10. That means that the digit in the next *higher* place will *also* increase by one.

Here is a simpler way to understand it: just look at the *two* (or three or four) digits to the left of your rounding line, and increase that "number" by one:

$$329,509 \approx 330,000 \qquad 998,271 \approx 1,000,000 \qquad 639,995 \approx 640,000$$

The "29" changes to "30".   The "99" changes to "100".   The "3999" changes to "4000".

2. Round the numbers as the dashed line indicates (to the underlined digit).

a. 10,9̲65 ≈	b. 89,506 ≈	c. 79̲7,329 ≈
d. 299,850 ≈	e. 254,99̲7 ≈	f. 599,9̲72 ≈

3. Round the numbers to the underlined place value unit.

a. 233,5̲64 ≈	b. 752,493 ≈	c. 19̲2,392 ≈
d. 89̲5,080 ≈	e. 8̲55,429 ≈	f. 399,477 ≈

4. Round these numbers to the nearest thousand, nearest ten thousand, and nearest hundred thousand.

number	274,302	596,253	709,932	899,430
to the nearest 1,000				
to the nearest 10,000				
to the nearest 100,000				

5. Round the numbers to the nearest hundred. *(Note: The numbers below take into account how many leap years you have likely lived.)*

   a. In 5 years, you have likely lived 1,826 days, or about _____ days.

   b. In 9 years, you have likely lived 3,287 days, or about _____ days.

   c. In 10 years, you have likely lived 3,652 days, or about _____ days.

   d. In 20 years, you have likely lived 7,305 days, or about _____ days.

   e. In 40 years, you have likely lived _____ days, or about _____ days.

   f. A challenge: figure out about how many days your mom, dad, or teacher has lived.

One more "quirky" thing. Let's say you are asked to round 284 to the nearest *thousand*. Notice that 284 does *not* have any thousands! We can say it has zero thousands and write it as 0,284 to show that.

Now, 0,284 ≈ 0,000 or just plain 0. But notice that 0,603 ≈ 1,000: it is rounded up to one thousand.

Similarly, rounded to the nearest ten thousand, 284 ≈ 0. Or look at it this way: 00,284 ≈ 00,000. Of course, the same thing happens if you round it to any bigger place (such as to ten thousands).

6. Round the numbers to the nearest ten thousand.

a. 235 ≈	b. 18,299 ≈	c. 1,392 ≈

7. Round the numbers to the nearest thousand.

a. 865 ≈	b. 182 ≈	c. 5,633 ≈

8. Round the numbers to the nearest ten thousand.

a. 56,250 ≈	b. 5,392 ≈	c. 2,938 ≈
d. 708,344 ≈	e. 599 ≈	f. 44,800 ≈

9. Use rounded numbers to solve these problems.

a. *Round the numbers to the nearest thousand.*

There are 235,792 people in Purpletown and 187,203 people in Bluetown.

This means there are about _____ people in Purpletown, and about _____ people

in Bluetown. The two towns have approximately _____ people in all.

There are about _____ more people in Purpletown than in Bluetown.

b. *Round the numbers to the nearest hundred.*

Last year, there were 2,384 live births in Seagull hospital and 1,094 in Sunshine hospital.

There were about _____ live births in total in those two. Seagull hospital had

about _____ more births than Sunshine hospital.

c. *Round the numbers to the nearest hundred.*

The Nile river (in Africa) is 6,695 km long and the Danube river (in Europe) 2,857 km long.

The Nile is about _____ km longer than the Danube.

10. The table lists some tall buildings and their heights.

    a. Round the height of each building to the nearest hundred feet.

    b. Use the *rounded* numbers. How many copies of Empire State Building would you need to place one on top of another, in order to exceed the height of Burj Khalifa?

    c. About how much taller is Burj Khalifa than Taipei 101?

Building	Height	Height (rounded)
Burj Khalifa	2,717 ft	
Shanghai Tower	2,073 ft	
Taipei 101	1,667 ft	
One World Trade Center	1,776 ft	
Petronas Tower 1	1,483 ft	
Empire State Building	1,250 ft	

11. If you travel around the earth one time on the equator, your trip is 24,900 miles long. The Moon lies at an average distance of 238,857 miles from the Earth.

    a. Round the two numbers to the nearest thousand in the spaces below:

    The trip around the equator is about _____ miles.

    The Moon is about _____ miles from the Earth.

    b. How many trips around the equator would be a longer distance than the distance from the Earth to the Moon? Solve this with the help of the table below.

Trips Around The Equator	Approximate Distance (miles)	Trips Around The Equator	Approximate Distance (miles)	Trips Around The Equator	Approximate Distance (miles)
1		5		9	
2	50,000	6	150,000	10	
3		7		11	
4		8		12	

Puzzle Corner Round each number so that you can solve each problem with mental math.

a. Jake's yearly earnings are $47,807.

That means about $_____.

So, he earns about _____ *monthly*.

b. Jack drove 58,496 miles last year.

That is about _____ miles. This means

he drives about _____ each *month*.

72

Multiples of 10, 100, and 1,000

Remember the shortcut? To multiply any number by ten, write the number and tag a zero to it.

For example: $78 \times 10 = \underline{780}$ or $10 \times 70 = \underline{700}$

1. Multiply by 10.

a. $11 \times 10 =$ _____	**b.** $50 \times 10 =$ _____	**c.** $200 \times 10 =$ _____
$29 \times 10 =$ _____	$80 \times 10 =$ _____	$1000 \times 10 =$ _____

2. Multiply by 100. Also, try to find a shortcut for multiplying any number by 100.
   Don't look ahead—try to do this yourself!

a. $7 \times 100 =$ _____	**b.** $10 \times 100 =$ _____	**c.** $20 \times 100 =$ _____
$9 \times 100 =$ _____	$13 \times 100 =$ _____	$22 \times 100 =$ _____

SHORTCUT: To multiply any number by one hundred, write the number, and tag two zeros to the end of it.

For example: $61 \times 100 = \underline{61}00$ and $100 \times \underline{410} = \underline{41,0}00$

SHORTCUT: To multiply any number by one thousand, write the number, and tag three zeros to the end of it.

For example: $98 \times 1,000 = \underline{98},000$ and $1000 \times \underline{277} = \underline{277},000$

3. Multiply.

a. $311 \times 100 =$ _____	**b.** $10 \times 19 =$ _____	**c.** $60 \times 1,000 =$ _____
$70 \times 100 =$ _____	$999 \times 10 =$ _____	$493 \times 1,000 =$ _____
$120 \times 100 =$ _____	$10 \times 4,500 =$ _____	$1,000 \times 500 =$ _____

4. Write using numbers.

a. 49 thousands _____	**b.** 20 tens _____	**c.** 37 tens _____
49 hundreds _____	20 hundreds _____	37 hundreds _____
49 tens _____	20 thousands _____	37 thousands _____

5. Write with numbers. What do we usually call...

a. 10 tens _____	b. 10 hundreds _____	c. 100 thousands _____
100 tens _____	100 hundreds _____	1,000 thousands _____

6. **a.** How many dollars do you have in a stack of forty 100-dollar bills?

   b. How many dollars do you have in a stack of fifty 10-dollar bills?

   c. How many dollars do you have in a stack of two hundred 100-dollar bills?

7. Write numbers inside parentheses.

   a. "Columbus landed in America in fourteen hundred ninety two. (_____)"

   b. "Andrew's car cost twenty-five hundred dollars (_____) when he got it
   but he is going to sell it for twelve hundred (_____)."

   c. "My great-great-grandfather was born in the year nineteen hundred (_____),
   and died in the year nineteen hundred sixty (_____)."

8. Now use the shortcuts "backwards." You can guess and check!

a. $67 \times$ _____ $= 670$	b. $112 \times$ _____ $= 11,200$	c. _____ $\times 100 = 4,400$
$18 \times$ _____ $= 1,800$	$80 \times$ _____ $= 80,000$	_____ $\times 10 = 900$
$20 \times$ _____ $= 200$	$390 \times$ _____ $= 3,900$	_____ $\times 1,000 = 60,000$

> In question 8 above, you were essentially doing <u>division problems</u>. Why? Because division is the same as doing multiplication "backwards"! They are opposite operations.
>
> So, finding a missing number (a missing factor) in a multiplication problem is the same as solving a division problem. See the examples below.
>
> **Example 1.** _____ $\times 10 = 600$ has the same answer as $600 \div 10 =$ _____.
>
> **Example 2.** $7,500 \div 100$ has the same answer as the problem _____ $\times 100 = 7,500$.

9. Think of multiplication in order to solve these divisions. You can guess, and multiply to check.

a. $120 \div 10 =$ _____	b. $700 \div 100 =$ _____	c. $12,000 \div 1000 =$ _____
$600 \div 10 =$ _____	$5,600 \div 100 =$ _____	$689,000 \div 1000 =$ _____
$1,300 \div 10 =$ _____	$65,000 \div 100 =$ _____	$400,000 \div 1000 =$ _____

10. Fill in.

a.

90	= 9 × 10
100	= 10 × 10
110	= _____ × 10

These are **multiples of 10**...	...because you get them if you *multiply* some number by 10.

280	= _____ × 10
1,000	= _____ × 10
4,560	= _____ × 10

b.

900	= 9 × 100
1000	= _____ × 100
1,100	= _____ × 100

These are **multiples of 100**...	...because you get them if you *multiply* some number by 100.

4,000	= _____ × 100
5,900	= _____ × 100
10,000	= _____ × 100

c.

10,000	= _____ × 1000
15,000	= _____ × 1000
18,000	= _____ × 1000

These are **multiples of 1,000**...	...because you get them if you *multiply* some number by 1,000.

50,000	= _____ × 1000
160,000	= _____ × 1000
520,000	= _____ × 1000

11. Notice - special things about multiples of 10, 100, and 1,000: ALL multiples of 10 end in ___.

ALL multiples of 100 end in _____.   ALL multiples of 1000 end in _____.

12. Fill in the table. You can use any multiples of ten and any multiples of 100 that you like, except they should be different from the numbers used in question 10.

Multiples of ten	What number times 10?
	= _____ × 10
	= _____ × 10
	= _____ × 10

Multiples of hundred	What number times 100?
	= _____ × 100
	= _____ × 100
	= _____ × 100

13. Divide. (In reality, simply think of multiplication.)

a. 1,000 ÷ 100 = _____	**b.** 90 ÷ 10 = _____	**c.** 2,000 ÷ 1,000 = _____
2,100 ÷ 100 = _____	7,000 ÷ 10 = _____	30,000 ÷ 1,000 = _____
99,900 ÷ 100 = _____	34,800 ÷ 10 = _____	342,000 ÷ 1,000 = _____

Puzzle Corner   About 10,000 average-sized human cells can fit on the head of a pin. About how many would fit on ten pinheads?

On twenty?   On thirty?

75

Mixed Review Chapter 2

1. Write the numbers given in the problem in the bar model. Write x in the bar model for the unknown (what the problem asks for). Then write a number sentence using x and solve it.

   (Bar Models in Addition and Subtraction/Ch.1)

   Edward bought a raincoat for $23.50 and rubber boots
   for $19.90. He paid and received $6.60 as change.
   What denomination of a bill did Edward use to pay?

   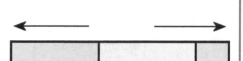

   _____

   $x =$ _____

2. Subtract the money amounts. Check by adding. (Calculate and Estimate Money Amounts /Ch.1)

a.	b.
$\begin{aligned}\$100.00\\-\quad 43.75\end{aligned}$ $+$ _____	$\begin{aligned}\$800.00\\-\ 516.99\end{aligned}$ $+$ _____

3. Which number sentence matches the problem? (Order of Operations /Ch.1)

   Rakes that cost $15 are discounted by $3.
   You buy four of them. What is the total cost?

   $(\$15 - \$3) \times 4$

   $4 \times \$15 - \$3$

   $(\$15 - \$4) \times 3$

   $\$15 - 4 \times \$3$

4. Write the numbers in order from the smallest to the greatest: (Comparing with Thousands/Ch.2)

   525,009   25,925   5,209   25,539

5. Either the number you subtract or the number you subtract from is unknown. Solve.

   (Bar Models in Addition and Subtraction/Ch.1)

a. $92 - x = 45$	b. $x - 566 = 700$	c. $900 - x = 267$
$x =$ _____	$x =$ _____	$x =$ _____

6. Solve. Write a number sentence for each problem, not just the answer.

---

a. Mike had $38. Then Grandma gave him some money, and
now he has $158. How much money did Grandma give him?

_____

---

b. Jill bought three magazines that cost $4 each with her some of her birthday money.
Now she has $28 left. How much money did she get for her birthday?

_____

---

c. Greg bought two books that cost $11 each with his birthday money.
He had $60. How much money does he have left?

_____

---

d. Dad bought each of his three children an ice cream cone that cost $0.60
and an ice cream cone for himself that cost $0.80. How much was the total?

_____

What was his change from $10?

_____

---

7. Write the numbers in expanded form. (Place Value with Thousands/Ch.2)

a. 68,056

b. 815,224

8. Round to the nearest dollar. (Calculate and Estimate Money Amounts/Ch.1)

a. $1.05 ≈ _____   **b.** $7.72 ≈ _____   **c.** $35.17 ≈ _____   **d.** $165.83 ≈ _____

e. $94.90 ≈ _____   **f.** $99.09 ≈ _____   **g.** $99.90 ≈ _____   **h.** $100.56 ≈ _____

9. Estimate the total cost using rounded numbers. Do *not* find the exact cost.
(Calculate and Estimate Money Amounts/Ch.1)

---

a. a computer math game $19.85; a dictionary $14.90; an encyclopedia on a CD $25.28

---

b. 4,000 marker pens at $0.98 each, and 1,000 whiteboard erasers at $1.02 each.

Review Chapter 2

1. Write the numbers.

a. 13 thousand   4 ones
   9 tens
	b. 300 thousand 5 tens
	   6 thousand
		c. 1 million

2. Write the numbers.

   a. 785 thousand 3 hundred   **b.** 70 thousand eight

3. What is the value of the digit 3 in the following numbers?

   a. 21<u>3</u>,047   **b.** 94,0<u>3</u>2

   c. <u>3</u>00,049   **d.** 9<u>3</u>2,255

4. Round these numbers to the nearest thousand and nearest ten thousand.

n	78,974	5,367	2,558	407,409	299,603
rounded to nearest 1,000					
rounded to nearest 10,000					

5. First estimate the result of $5,076 - 2,845 - 675$ by rounding the numbers to the nearest hundred. Then find the exact answer.

   Estimation:

   Exact answer:

6. Find the missing numbers.

    a. $40{,}505 = 5 + $ _____ $ + 40{,}000$ **b.** $796{,}000 = 96{,}000 + $ _____

    c. $4{,}605{,}506 = 500 + 5{,}000 + 4{,}000{,}000 + 6 + $ _____

7. Write $<$ or $>$ between the numbers.

a. 5,406 5,604	**b.** 49530 49553	**c.** 605748 60584

8. Write the numbers in order from the smallest to the greatest.

    5,905,544   95,695   495,644   496,455   145,900   590,554

9. Calculate. Line up all of the place values carefully.

        a. $355{,}399 + 2{,}455 + 34{,}200$ **b.** $490{,}213 - 45{,}344$

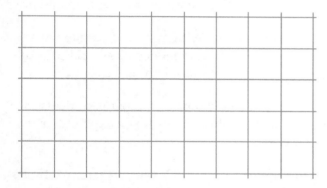 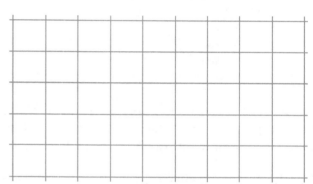

10. A banker puts five hundred $100-bills in a briefcase.
    What is the total amount in dollars?
    Write a multiplication.

11. Mark earns $2,560 in a month.
    How much does he earn in ten months?

    How much does he earn in two months?

    And lastly, how much does he earn in 12 months?

Chapter 3: Multi-Digit Multiplication
Introduction

The third chapter of *Math Mammoth Grade 4* covers multi-digit multiplication and some related topics. This is one of the focus areas of 4th grade math. For further help in teaching these topics, check out the free videos matched to the curriculum at **https://www.mathmammoth.com/videos/**.

The first lessons briefly review the multiplication concept and the times tables. The next lesson, where students solve scales or pan balance problems, is intended to be somewhat fun and motivational. The balance problems are actually equations in disguise. The focus of the chapter is multi-digit multiplication. We start out by multiplying numbers by whole tens and hundreds (such as 20×4 or 500×6). After this, students learn multiplication part-by-part (also called partial products) — a very important concept. It means that we calculate, for example, 4×63 in two parts: first we solve 4×60 and 4×3, and then we add the two results ($240 + 12 = 252$).

This principle underlies the standard multiplication algorithm and it also allows us to calculate the result of a multiplication mentally, so it is very important to master. Additionally, multiplying in parts is tied in with an area model — which also is important to learn. Before learning the traditional form of the multiplication algorithm, students encounter a simplified form of that algorithm in the lesson *Multiply in Columns—the Easy Way*. At your discretion, you may skip that lesson or skim through it quickly, if your student is ready to understand the standard form of the algorithm, which is taught next.

Students also study estimation, the order of operations, and multiplying with money. These lessons have numerous word problems. Students are instructed to write a number sentence or several for each word problem, which helps them learn how to show their work for math problems.

The idea in the lesson *So Many of the Same Thing* is very simple, yet it actually prepares students to study proportions (in middle school math). In this lesson, students fill in values for two quantities in tables (for example, the quantity of the items and the total cost).

Near the end of the chapter, we study 2-digit by 2-digit multiplication (e.g. 52×63). Again, we first use partial products, including in the context of an area model. The lesson *Multiplying in Parts: Another Way* presents an alternate way to multiply and is optional. After that we end the chapter with the standard algorithm for multiplying a two-digit number by a two-digit number.

The Lessons in Chapter 3

Helpful Resources on the Internet

You can also access this list of links at https://l.mathmammoth.com/gr4ch3

DISCLAIMER: *We check these links a few times a year. However, we cannot guarantee that the links have not changed. Parental supervision is always recommended.*

Multiplication Tables — Online Practice
Ad-free online practice of the multiplication tables at MathMammoth.com website. Also works as an offline program in most browsers. Includes the option for both timed and non-timed practice.
https://www.mathmammoth.com/practice/multiplication.php

Multiplication games for the multiplication tables
Improve your multiplication skills with these fun games!
https://www.multiplication.com/games/all-games

https://www.hoodamath.com/games/multiplication.html

Interactive Pan Balance
Each of the four shapes is assigned a certain (unknown) weight. You need to figure out their weights by placing them on the two sides of the pan balance in different configurations.
https://www.nctm.org/Classroom-Resources/Illuminations/Interactives/Pan-Balance----Shapes/

Stable Scales Quiz
In each picture, the scales are balanced. Can you find the weight of the items on the scales?
https://www.transum.org/Software/SW/Starter_of_the_day/Students/Stable_Scales_Quiz.asp

MULTIPLYING IN PARTS (PARTIAL PRODUCTS)

Mental Multiplication of Multiples of 10 and 100
This activity allows you to rehearse the mental multiplication of multiples of 10 and 100, e.g. 30 × 400 etc. Play against the clock and see what level you can get up to before you run out of time!
https://www.studyzone.tv/game86-code3dc5617c60ff2ca509aabc60944162d1

Area Model Multiplication
Build rectangles of various sizes and relate multiplication to area. Discover new strategies for multiplying large numbers. Use the game screen to test your problem solving strategies!
https://phet.colorado.edu/en/simulation/area-model-multiplication

Partial Products Finder App
An interactive app that illustrates multiplication (up to 30 x 30) with an area model.
https://apps.mathlearningcenter.org/partial-product-finder/

Multiply 2-Digits by 1-Digit with Area Models – from Khan Academy
Practice multiplying in parts with the aid of area models.
https://bit.ly/multiply-area-models

MULTIPLICATION ALGORITHM

One-Digit by Two-Digits Multiplication Game
Students will multiply one-digit numbers by two-digit whole numbers, then get to try to shoot a basket.
https://www.math-play.com/one-digit-by-two-digit-multiplication-game/one-digit-by-two-digit-multiplication-game_html5.html

Multiplication Jeopardy Game
You get to solve multi-digit multiplication questions of 1-digit by 1-digit, 1-digit by 2-digit, and 1-digit by 3-digit numbers in this game.
https://www.math-play.com/Multiplicaton-Jeopardy/multiplication-game_html5.html

Canoe Penguins
Answer the multiplication problems quickly and correctly to help your penguins win the race!
https://www.arcademics.com/games/canoe-penguins

Batter's Up Baseball
Answer the multiplication problems correctly to help the home team beat the visiting team. Choose "Double" or "Homerun" level.
https://prongo.com/baseball-multiply/

Multi-Digit Multiplication Practice
Practice vertical (column) multiplication with this fun and colorful online game!
https://www.mathmammoth.com/practice/vertical-multiplication

Multi-Digit Multiplication Number Battle Card Game
Arrange your cards to make the highest product possible.
https://booksmartmath.com/wp-content/uploads/2020/04/Multi-Digit-Multiplication-Number-Battle.pdf

Multiplication Quiz
Practice multiplying by one digit in this 10-question online quiz.
https://www.thatquiz.org/tq-1/?-jg24-la-p0

Math FROG MultipliACTION
Practice 2 by 2 digit multiplication online. Enter one digit in each box.
https://cemc2.math.uwaterloo.ca/mathfrog/english/kidz/mult5.shtml

Math Computation Practice: Multiply Two digits by Two Digits
Practice two-digit multiplication in columns.
https://www.mathplayground.com/multiplication05.html

ORDER OF OPERATIONS

Choose Math Operation
Choose the operation(s) so that the number sentence is true. Helps develop number sense and logical thinking.
https://www.homeschoolmath.net/operation-game.php

Order of Ops
Save seven members of a Royal Family from prison by using your order of operation skills. Choose the expression to be solved in each step, and solve it. The program uses a visual representation of a stairway to show how the expression gets shorter at each step.
https://mrnussbaum.com/order-ops-online-game

Order of Operations Quiz
A 10-question online quiz that includes two different operations and possibly parentheses in each question. You can also modify the quiz parameters yourself.
https://www.thatquiz.org/tq-1/?-j8f-la

Exploring Order of Operations (Object Interactive)
Click on the operation to be done first in the given expression. The program then solves that, and you click on the *next* operation to be performed, etc., until it is solved. The resource also includes a game. Note: Loads slowly in Chrome, and doesn't work in Firefox.
https://www.learnalberta.ca/content/mejhm/html/object_interactives/order_of_operations/use_it.html

Order of Operations Practice
A simple online quiz of 10 questions. Uses parentheses and the four operations.
https://www.onlinemathlearning.com/order-of-operations-practice.html

MISCELLANEOUS

Multiplication Matching Game
Practice the multiplication tables while also uncovering a hidden picture in this fun matching game!
https://www.mathmammoth.com/practice/multiplication-matching

Unitary Method
Answers questions involving simple proportions in this interactive self-check activity.
https://www.transum.org/software/SW/Starter_of_the_day/Students/Unitary_Method.asp

Thinking Blocks
Thinking Blocks is an engaging, interactive math tool that helps students learn how to solve multi-step word problems. Choose "Thinking Blocks Multiplication".
https://www.mathplayground.com/thinkingblocks.html

Multiplication Word Problem Quiz
This 10-question quiz focuses on using multiplication to solve word problems.
https://www.softschools.com/quizzes/math/multiplication_word_problems/quiz1059.html

7 practical tips for mental math (that ANYONE can use!)
People with number sense use numbers flexibly, and EVERYONE can learn these mental math strategies to improve their number sense.
https://www.mathmammoth.com/lessons/practical_tips_mental_math.php

Understanding Multiplication

- Multiplication has to do with many groups of the same size: 3×5 means three groups of 5. You can find the total by adding: $3 \times 5 = 5 + 5 + 5 = 15$.

- Multiplying by 1 means you have just one group: $1 \times 17 = 17$.

- Multiplying by 0 means "no groups": $0 \times 82 = 0$

- The order in which you multiply does not matter: 3×6 and 6×3 are both 18.

3 groups of 6 *or* 6 groups of 3.

1. Write the additions as multiplications, or vice versa. Solve.

a. $2 + 2 + 2 + 2 = \underline{2} \times \underline{4} = \underline{8}$

$20 + 20 + 20 + 20 = \underline{20} \times \underline{4} = \underline{80}$

b. $8 + 8 + 8 = \underline{8} \times \underline{3} = \underline{24}$

$80 + 80 + 80 = \underline{80} \times \underline{3} = \underline{2400}$

c. $\underline{500+500+500+500} = 4 \times 500 = \underline{2000}$

$\underline{120+120+120} = 3 \times 120 = \underline{360}$

2. Write two multiplications.

a. $\underline{3} \times \underline{6} = \underline{18}$

$\underline{6} \times \underline{3} = \underline{18}$

b. $\underline{1} \times \underline{5} = \underline{5}$

$\underline{5} \times \underline{1} = \underline{5}$

3. Solve.

a. $8 \times 2 = \underline{16}$

$8 \times 0 \times 7 = \underline{0}$

b. $3 \times 5 = \underline{15}$

$1 \times 2 \times 5 = \underline{10}$

c. $2 \times 8 = \underline{16}$

$2 \times 2 \times 2 = \underline{8}$

d. $3 \times 10 = \underline{30}$

$|3 \times 3| \times 3 = \underline{27}$

$9 \times 3 =$

4. Find the products. You can often use addition.

a.	b.	c.	d.
$2 \times 24 = \underline{48}$	$2 \times 150 = \underline{300}$	$4 \times 1{,}000 = \underline{4{,}000}$	$2 \times 34 = \underline{68}$
$14 \times 0 = \underline{0}$	$3 \times 2{,}000 = \underline{6{,}000}$	$5 \times 200 = \underline{1{,}000}$	$3 \times 21 = \underline{63}$
$16 \times 1 = \underline{16}$	$4 \times 3{,}000 = \underline{12{,}000}$	$3 \times 211 = \underline{633}$	$4 \times 50 = \underline{200}$

Multiplication terms

The numbers being multiplied are **factors**.
The result is called a **product**.

There may be more than two factors. For example, in
$4 \times 5 \times 2 = 40$, the numbers 4, 5, and 2 are all factors.

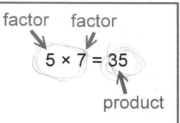

5. Find the unknown factors.

a. $\underline{6} \times 2 \times 2 = 24$ $\underline{0} \times 9 \times 2 = 0$	b. $3 \times \underline{200} = 600$ $4 \times \underline{250} = \boxed{1,000}$	c. $500 \times \underline{3} = 1,500$ $10 \times \underline{81} = 810$

6. Fill in.

a. Write the the terms. $2 \times 23 = 46$ $\uparrow$ $\uparrow$ $\uparrow$ <u>factor</u> <u>product</u>	b. Write a multiplication problem with factors 4 and 8. $4 \times 8 = 32$
c. What happens if one of the factors is zero? The <u>Product</u> is <u>Zero</u>.	
d. In one multiplication problem, two factors are 2 and 6. The product is 60. What is the third factor? $2 \times 6 \times 5 = 60$	

7. Write a number sentence for each of these problems. Use several operations in it.

Problem:	Number sentence:
a. Mom had three dozen eggs in cartons and five in a bowl. How many eggs did she have in all?	$3 \times 12 + 5 = 41$
b. Jack bought six packages of magazines. Each had 10 magazines. He opened one package and gave three magazines to his friend. How many magazines does Jack have left?	$6 \times 10 - 3 = 57$
c. Anna had seven boxes. Into four of the boxes, she put 10 crayons each, and into three boxes she put only 6. How many crayons did she use?	$4 \times 10 + 3 \times 6 =$ $40 + 18 = 58 \text{ crayons}$
d. Ernest bought three books for $11 each and paid with $50. What was his change?	$3 \times 11 = 33$, $50 - 33 = 17$ 17 in change
e. How many wheels do five tricycles and seven bikes have in total?	$3 \times 5 = 15$ $7 \times 2 = 14$ $14 + 15 = 29$ wheels

Example. A simple hat costs $6. Another, fancier hat, costs $18. How many times more expensive is the fancier hat?

It asks "how many times", so that is our unknown (?). We write a multiplication:

$$\underline{\ ?\ } \times 6 = \$18$$

It is easy to see the answer is three times, or ? = 3.

8. Solve the problems. Write a multiplication <u>with an unknown</u> (? or y) for each problem. What is the unknown in each problem? It is what the problem asks for or what you do not know.
   (Note also: we are not using x as an unknown, as it could be confused with the multiplication sign ?.)

a. Each child has 10 toes. How many toes would seven children have? $\underline{10} \times \underline{7} = \underline{?}$ $\underline{?} = \underline{70}$	**b.** If each cow has four feet, how many cows are there if there is a total of 24 feet? $\underline{?} \times \underline{4} = \underline{24}$ $\underline{?} = \underline{6}$
c. One bicycle has two wheels. $\underline{?}$ bicycles have 18 wheels. $\underline{?} \times \underline{2} = \underline{18}$ $\underline{?} = \underline{4}$	**d.** One car has 4 wheels. So, y cars have 36 wheels. $\underline{y} \times \underline{4} = \underline{36}$ $y = \underline{9}$
e. How many people would you need to have a total of 150 fingers? $\underline{y} \times \underline{10} = \underline{150}$ $y = \underline{15}$	**f.** How many dozen eggs would be 60 eggs? $\underline{y} \times \underline{12} = \underline{60}$ $y = \underline{5}$
g. Carl owns 20 children's books. Emma owns four times as many children's books. How many children's books does Emma own? $\underline{20} \times \underline{4} = \underline{y}$ $y = \underline{80}$	**h.** You can fit 7 people in a van. How many such vans do you need to take 35 people to the beach? $\underline{7} \times \underline{y} = \underline{35}$ $y = \underline{5}$
i. A track in the woods is 300 yards long. Another track is 1,200 yards long. How many times longer is the second track than the first? $\underline{300} \times \underline{y} = \underline{1,200}$ $y = \underline{4}$	**j.** Margaret has made 40 cups of jelly and she puts it in pint jars. How many jars will be filled? $\underline{y} \times \underline{2} = \underline{40}$ $y = \underline{20}$

Multiplication Tables Review

Why is it important to learn your multiplication tables? Why couldn't you just use addition or other ways to find what is 6 × 9, 7 × 8, or 4 × 7? There are several reasons:

1. The knowledge of multiplication tables is needed for the opposite operation: division. Once you know the tables, you can do divisions such as 54 ÷ 6 or 56 ÷ 7 quickly in your head.

2. You also need to know the multiplication tables in order to perform long division.

3. Knowing the tables helps you be able to quickly simplify fractions. For example, you need to be able *to immediately* notice that both numbers in the fraction $\frac{56}{64}$ are in the table of 8.

4. Fraction addition and subtraction are very difficult if you don't know your tables by heart.

5. The tables are also necessary to be able to find factors and prime factorization of numbers.

1. Fill in the multiplication tables below and answer the questions.

1 × 5 = 5	7 × 5 = 35
2 × 5 = 10	8 × 5 = 40
3 × 5 = 15	9 × 5 = 45
4 × 5 = 20	10 × 5 = 50
5 × 5 = 25	11 × 5 = 55
6 × 5 = 30	12 × 5 = 60

1 × 10 = 10	7 × 10 = 70
2 × 10 = 20	8 × 10 = 80
3 × 10 = 30	9 × 10 = 90
4 × 10 = 40	10 × 10 = 100
5 × 10 = 50	11 × 10 = 110
6 × 10 = 60	12 × 10 = 120

1 × 11 = 11	7 × 11 = 77
2 × 11 = 22	8 × 11 = 88
3 × 11 = 33	9 × 11 = 99
4 × 11 = 44	10 × 11 = 110
5 × 11 = 55	11 × 11 = 111
6 × 11 = 66	12 × 11 = 112

To find a number times 5, first multiply that number by 10, and take half of that. So for 7 × 5, first go 7 × 10 = 70 and take half of that.

Elevens are as easy as pie!

2. What same answers do you find in the tables of 5 and 10? Why?

1 × 2 = 2	7 × 2 = 14
2 × 2 = 4	8 × 2 = 16
3 × 2 = 6	9 × 2 = 18
4 × 2 = 8	10 × 2 = 20
5 × 2 = 10	11 × 2 = 22
6 × 2 = 12	12 × 2 = 24

1 × 4 = 4	7 × 4 = 28
2 × 4 = 8	8 × 4 = 32
3 × 4 = 12	9 × 4 = 36
4 × 4 = 16	10 × 4 = 40
5 × 4 = 20	11 × 4 = 44
6 × 4 = 24	12 × 4 = 48

1 × 8 = 8	7 × 8 = 56
2 × 8 = 16	8 × 8 = 64
3 × 8 = 24	9 × 8 = 72
4 × 8 = 32	10 × 8 = 80
5 × 8 = 40	11 × 8 = 88
6 × 8 = 48	12 × 8 = 96

What same answers (products) do you find in the tables of 2, 4, and 8?

They go

To find a number times 4, you can double it twice:

Example. 7 × 4 = ?? Double 7 is 14, then double that to get 28.

You can double a number three times to find these. For example, to find 6 × 8, find double 6, and double that, then double that.

5, 6, 7, 8 — fifty-six is 7 times 8.

Color ones digits one color and tens digits another. You will see a pattern.

3. Fill in the multiplication tables below and answer the questions.

$1 \times 3 = 3$	$7 \times 3 = 21$	$1 \times 6 = 6$	$7 \times 6 = 42$
$2 \times 3 = 6$	$8 \times 3 = 24$	$2 \times 6 = 12$	$8 \times 6 = 48$
$3 \times 3 = 9$	$9 \times 3 = 27$	$3 \times 6 = 18$	$9 \times 6 = 54$
$4 \times 3 = 12$	$10 \times 3 = 30$	$4 \times 6 = 24$	$10 \times 6 = 60$
$5 \times 3 = 15$	$11 \times 3 = 33$	$5 \times 6 = 30$	$11 \times 6 = 66$
$6 \times 3 = 18$	$12 \times 3 = 36$	$6 \times 6 = 36$	$12 \times 6 = 72$

$1 \times 9 = 9$	$7 \times 9 = 63$
$2 \times 9 = 18$	$8 \times 9 = 72$
$3 \times 9 = 27$	$9 \times 9 = 81$
$4 \times 9 = 36$	$10 \times 9 = 90$
$5 \times 9 = 45$	$11 \times 9 = 99$
$6 \times 9 = 54$	$12 \times 9 = 108$

To find a number times 6, you can double
the corresponding one from the table of 3:

$6 \times 7 = ??$ Find 3×7, and double that.

What same products do you find in the tables of 3 and 6?

Why is that?

The table of 9 has **special things**!

Color all the ones digits
yellow (of the answers).
Color all the tens digits
red (of the answers).

Add the digits of each answer.
What do you notice?

4. These are harder ones...
   but remember, you can
   change the order of
   multiplication.
   8×7 is the same as 7×8,
   which is 56.

$1 \times 7 = 7$	$7 \times 7 = 49$	$1 \times 12 = 12$	$7 \times 12 = 84$
$2 \times 7 = 14$	$8 \times 7 = 56$	$2 \times 12 = 24$	$8 \times 12 = 96$
$3 \times 7 = 21$	$9 \times 7 = 63$	$3 \times 12 = 36$	$9 \times 12 = 108$
$4 \times 7 = 28$	$10 \times 7 = 70$	$4 \times 12 = 48$	$10 \times 12 = 120$
$5 \times 7 = 35$	$11 \times 7 = 77$	$5 \times 12 = 60$	$11 \times 12 = 132$
$6 \times 7 = 42$	$12 \times 7 = 84$	$6 \times 12 = 72$	$12 \times 12 = 144$

5. It is time to test your knowledge with missing factor problems!

a. $7 \times 7 = 49$ $4 \times 7 = 28$ $8 \times 7 = 56$	**b.** $8 \times 6 = 48$ $5 \times 6 = 30$ $9 \times 6 = 54$	**c.** $8 \times 8 = 64$ $6 \times 8 = 48$ $7 \times 8 = 56$	**d.** $8 \times 9 = 72$ $6 \times 9 = 54$ $7 \times 9 = 63$
e. $9 \times 5 = 45$ $7 \times 5 = 35$ $8 \times 5 = 40$	**f.** $9 \times 3 = 27$ $6 \times 3 = 18$ $7 \times 3 = 21$	**g.** $7 \times 4 = 28$ $9 \times 4 = 36$ $8 \times 4 = 32$	**h.** $9 \times 2 = 18$ $8 \times 2 = 16$ $6 \times 2 = 12$
i. $5 \times 7 = 35$ $9 \times 7 = 63$ $3 \times 7 = 21$	**j.** $12 \times 5 = 60$ $5 \times 5 = 25$ $6 \times 5 = 30$	**k.** $6 \times 6 = 36$ $12 \times 6 = 72$ $7 \times 6 = 42$	**l.** $9 \times 8 = 72$ $2 \times 8 = 16$ $4 \times 8 = 32$

6. Fill in the table.

×	0	1	2	3	4	5	6	7	8	9	10	11	12
0	0	0	0	0	0	0	0	0	0	0	0	0	0
1	0	1	2	3	4	5	6	7	8	9	10	11	12
2	0	2	4	6	8	10	12	14	16	18	20	22	24
3	0	3	6	9	12	15	18	21	24	27	30	33	36
4	0	4	8	12	16	20	24	28	32	36	40	44	48
5	0	5	10	15	20	25	30	35	40	45	50	55	60
6	0	6	12	18	24	30	36	42	48	54	60	66	72
7	0	7	14	21	28	35	42	49	56	63	70	77	84
8	0	8	16	24	32	40	48	56	64	72	80	88	96
9	0	9	18	27	36	45	54	63	72	81	90	99	108
10	0	10	20	30	40	50	60	70	80	90	100	110	120
11	0	11	22	33	44	55	66	77	88	99	110	120	132
12	0	12	24	36	48	60	72	84	96	108	120	132	144

7. A school hired a bus and eight minivans to take the 90 students to a swimming pool.
   All the minivans were full, with 7 students in each.
   How many students went in the bus?

$8 \times 7 = 56$ $90 - 56 = 34$

$$\begin{array}{r} 8\,9\,0 \\ -\ 5\,6 \\ \hline 3\,4 \end{array}$$

8. Let's practice the order of operations again.

a. $4 \times 7 + 5 = $ _____	**c.** $4 \times (7 - 5) = $ _____	**e.** $(4 + 5) \times (5 + 2) = $ _____
b. $2 \times (5 + 6) + 4 = $ _____	**d.** $100 - 5 \times 6 = $ _____	**f.** $70 - (5 + 6) \times 4 = $ _____

9. Fill in the missing numbers so that both sides of the equals sign "=" have the same value.

Example: $2 \times 12 = 8 \times$ _3_ because $24 = 24$	**a.** $2 \times 6 = 4 \times$ _____ $12 = 12$	**b.** $6 \times 6 = 4 \times$ _____
c. $3 \times 10 = 6 \times$ _____	**d.** $2 \times 20 = 10 \times$ _____	**e.** $5 \times 12 = 6 \times$ _____

Scales Problems

This is a pan balance or scales. You put things into the two "pans," and the heavier pan will go down, like in a seesaw. If the two things weigh the same, the balance stays balanced.

We can use the pan balance to model simple equations with an unknown. In this lesson you will solve many equations with its help.

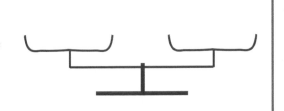

1. Solve how much each geometric shape "weighs." You can imagine the weights being so many pounds or kilograms, if it helps.

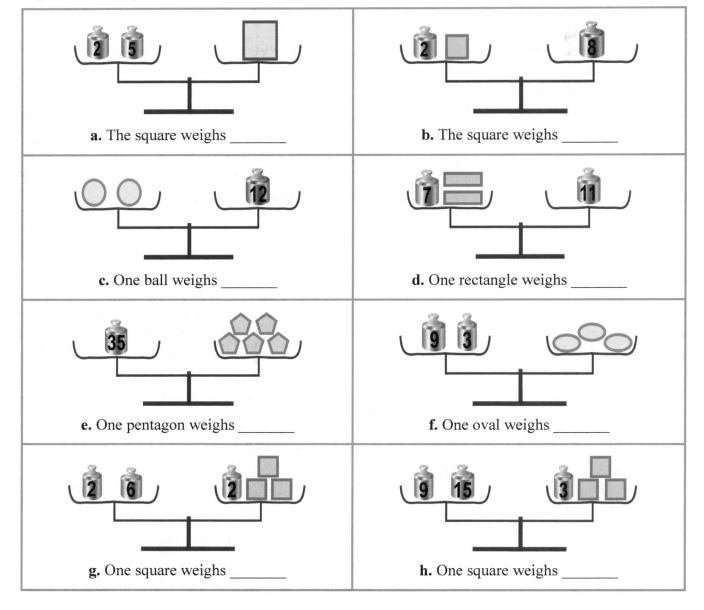

a. The square weighs _____

b. The square weighs _____

c. One ball weighs _____

d. One rectangle weighs _____

e. One pentagon weighs _____

f. One oval weighs _____

g. One square weighs _____

h. One square weighs _____

If there are "unknown shapes" on both sides, use this "trick":

Cross out the same amount of unknown shapes from both sides.

That way the balance will continue to stay balanced!

We cross out two diamonds from both sides.
Then we see that *three* diamonds weigh 15.
This of course means that one diamond weighs 5.

2. Solve the pan balance equations.

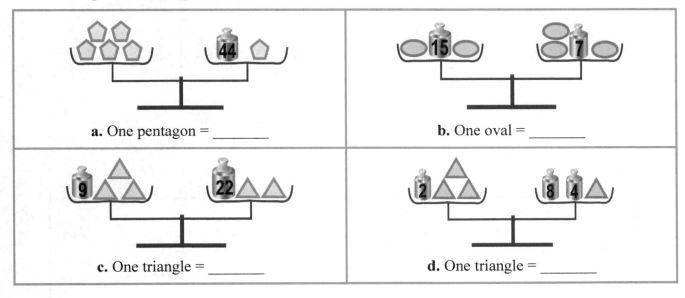

a. One pentagon = _____

b. One oval = _____

c. One triangle = _____

d. One triangle = _____

3. Solve. These are trickier. Use *both* balances to figure out the *two* unknown shapes.
   Guess and check! See the answer key for a hint.

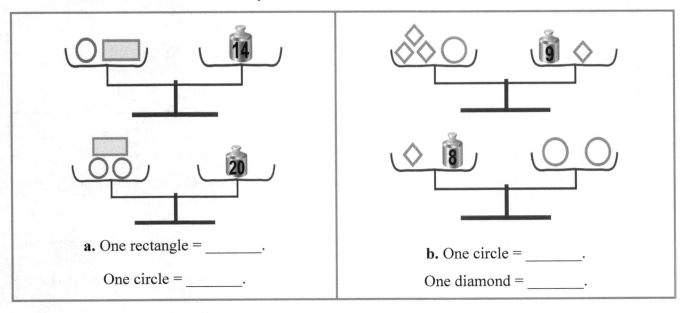

a. One rectangle = _____.

One circle = _____.

b. One circle = _____.

One diamond = _____.

91

4. These are double scales. Each scale on one side is like a puzzle in itself—so solve that first!

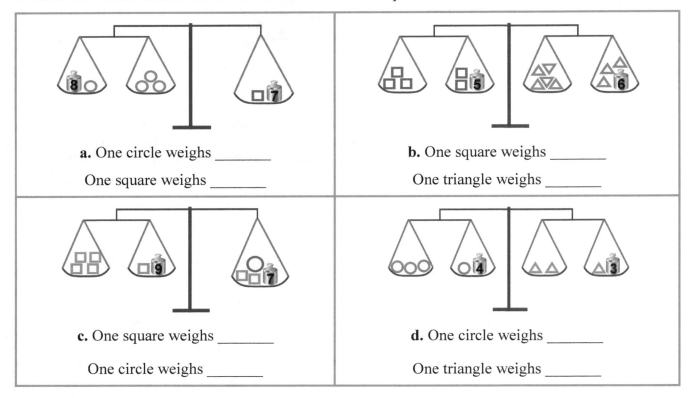

a. One circle weighs _____

One square weighs _____

b. One square weighs _____

One triangle weighs _____

c. One square weighs _____

One circle weighs _____

d. One circle weighs _____

One triangle weighs _____

In mathematics, the equal sign "=" is like a scales that is balanced. Something is on the right side, something else is on the left side, and the sides are equal or "balanced."

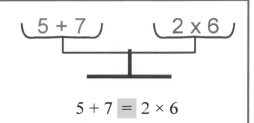

$$5 + 7 = 2 \times 6$$

5. Find the numbers that go on the empty lines. These equations are like little puzzles!

a. $78 + \underline{\quad} = 148$	**b.** $7 + 6 + 6 = \underline{\quad} - 10$	**c.** $2 \times 50 = 40 + \underline{\quad}$
d. $160 = \underline{\quad} + 9$	**e.** $5 + 5 + 5 + \underline{\quad} = 2 \times 12$	**f.** $7 \times 6 = 2 \times \underline{\quad}$
g. $50 - \underline{\quad} = 32$	**h.** $16 + 19 = 2 \times \underline{\quad} + 1$	**i.** $4 \times 6 - 7 = 2 \times \underline{\quad} + 1$

On the next page you will find pictures of empty scales. You can print out the page and make up your own problems but be careful! If you just make random problems, the solutions are likely to be fractions. See also:

http://mste.illinois.edu/users/pavel/java/balance/

https://www.transum.org/Software/SW/Starter_of_the_day/Students/Stable_Scales_Quiz.asp – weighing scales game that practices algebraic reasoning

https://www.nctm.org/Classroom-Resources/Illuminations/Interactives/Pan-Balance----Shapes/ – an interactive pan balance with shapes.

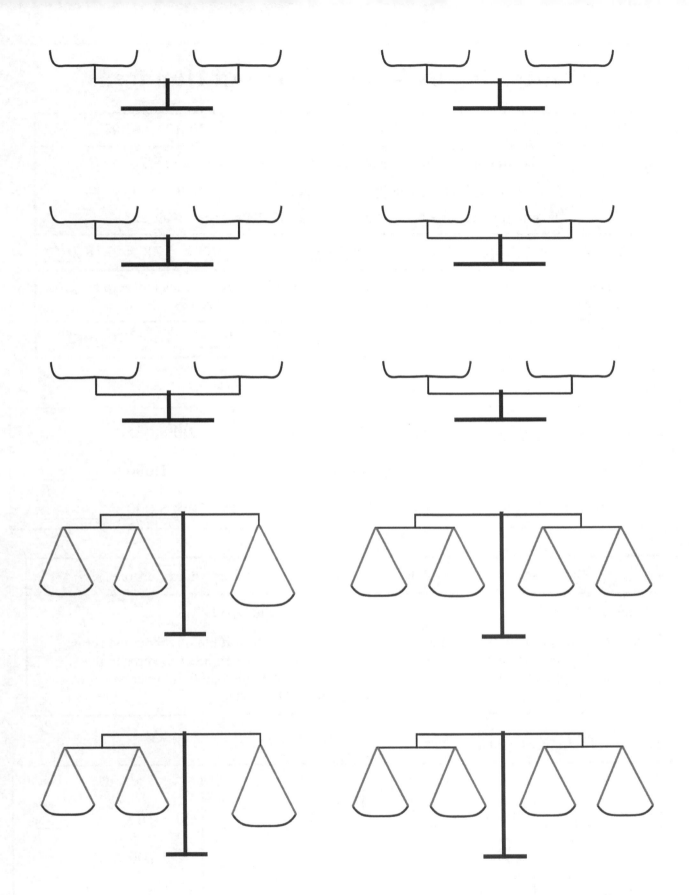

Multiplying by Whole Tens and Hundreds

We have studied the SHORTCUTS for multiplying any number by 10, 100, or 1,000:
To multiply any number by **10**, just tag **ONE zero** to the end.   To multiply any number by **100**, just tag **TWO zeros** to the end.   To multiply any number by **1,000**, just tag **THREE zeros** to the end.
$10 \times 481 = 4,810$ $100 \times 47 = 4,700$ $1000 \times 578 = 578,000$
Note especially what happens when the number you multiply already ends in a zero or zeros. The rule works the same way, and you *still* have to tag the zero or zeros.
$10 \times 800 = 8000$ $100 \times 6,600 = 660,000$ $1000 \times 40 = 40,000$

1. Multiply.

a. $10 \times 315 = $ _____	**b.** $100 \times 6,200 = $ _____	**c.** $1,000 \times 250 = $ _____
$3,560 \times 10 = $ _____	$10 \times 1,200 = $ _____	$38 \times 1,000 = $ _____
$35 \times 100 = $ _____	$100 \times 130 = $ _____	$10 \times 5,000 = $ _____

Shortcut for multiplying by 20 or 200 (You can probably guess this one!)	
What is 20 × 14? First solve the problem without the zero in 20: $2 \times 14 = 28$. Next, tag a zero to the answer, 28, and you get 280. So, $20 \times 14 = 280$.	**What is 200 × 31?** First solve the problem without the zeros: $2 \times 31 = 62$. Next, just *two* zeros to the result, 62, to get 6,200. In other words, $200 \times 31 = 6,200$.

2. Now try it! Multiply by 20 and 200.

a.	b.	c.	d.
$20 \times 8 = $ _____	$200 \times 7 = $ _____	$20 \times 12 = $ _____	$20 \times 16 = $ _____
$4 \times 20 = $ _____	$5 \times 200 = $ _____	$35 \times 20 = $ _____	$42 \times 200 = $ _____
$20 \times 5 = $ _____	$11 \times 200 = $ _____	$200 \times 9 = $ _____	$54 \times 20 = $ _____

Why does the shortcut work? It is based on the fact that we can multiply numbers in any order.

When multiplying any number by 20, we can write the 20 as 10×2. For example:	Let's try the same idea with 200. We will write 200 as 100×2. For example:

$$\underline{20} \times 14 = \underline{10 \times 2} \times 14$$

$$\underline{200} \times 31 = \underline{100 \times 2} \times 31$$

In that problem, first multiply $2 \times 14 = 28$. Then the problem becomes 10×28, which equals 280. Notice again how we did it:

In that problem, first multiply $2 \times 31 = 62$. The problem now becomes 100×62, which is 6,200. Notice again how it was done:

$$\underline{20} \times 14$$
$$= \underline{10} \times 2 \times 14$$
$$= 10 \times 28$$
$$= 280$$

$$\underline{200} \times 31$$
$$= \underline{100} \times 2 \times 31$$
$$= 100 \times 62$$
$$= 6,200$$

3. Try it yourself! Fill in.

a. 20×7	b. 20×5	c. 200×8	d. 200×25
$= \underline{\hspace{1cm}} \times 2 \times 7$	$= \underline{\hspace{1cm}} \times 2 \times 5$	$= \underline{\hspace{1cm}} \times 2 \times 8$	$= \underline{\hspace{1cm}} \times 2 \times 25$
$= 10 \times \underline{\hspace{1cm}}$	$= 10 \times \underline{\hspace{1cm}}$	$= 100 \times \underline{\hspace{1cm}}$	$= 100 \times \underline{\hspace{1cm}}$
$= \underline{\hspace{1cm}}$	$= \underline{\hspace{1cm}}$	$= \underline{\hspace{1cm}}$	$= \underline{\hspace{1cm}}$

4. Mark's shed measures 20 ft by 15 ft. Write and solve a number sentence for its area. ("A" means area.)

   A = _____

Hint: To calculate the area of a rectangle, multiply its two sides.

5. Write a number sentence to find the area of Mark's driveway, and solve it.

   A = _____

200 ft

15 ft

6. Mark was told he needed four truckloads of gravel to cover his driveway. *One* truckload costs $5 \times \$20$ plus \$30 for the delivery. How much will it cost him to cover the driveway with gravel?

SHORTCUT for multiplying by whole tens and whole hundreds	

The same principle works if you multiply by whole tens (30, 40, 50, 60, 70, 80, or 90): simply multiply by 3, 4, 5, 6, 7, 8, or 9, and then tag a zero to the result.

Similarly, if you multiply by some whole hundred, first solve the multiplication without the two zeros of the hundreds, and then tag two zeros to the result.

$50 \times 8 = 400$	$90 \times 11 = 990$	$300 \times 8 = 2{,}400$	$12 \times 800 = 9{,}600$

7. Multiply.

a. $40 \times 3 =$ _____ $8 \times 20 =$ _____	**b.** $70 \times 6 =$ _____ $50 \times 11 =$ _____	**c.** $80 \times 9 =$ _____ $30 \times 15 =$ _____
d. $60 \times 11 =$ _____ $12 \times 40 =$ _____	**e.** $200 \times 9 =$ _____ $7 \times 400 =$ _____	**f.** $700 \times 6 =$ _____ $600 \times 11 =$ _____
g. $200 \times 12 =$ _____ $15 \times 300 =$ _____	**h.** $3 \times 1100 =$ _____ $8 \times 900 =$ _____	**i.** $11 \times 120 =$ _____ $8 \times 300 =$ _____

It even works this way:		
To multiply 40×70, simply multiply 4×7, and tag two zeros to the result: $40 \times 70 = 2{,}800$	To multiply 600×40, simply multiply 6×4, and tag three zeros to the result: $600 \times 40 = 24{,}000$	To multiply 700×800, simply multiply 7×8, and tag four zeros to the result. $700 \times 800 = 560{,}000$

8. Multiply.

a. $20 \times 90 =$ _____ $70 \times 300 =$ _____	**b.** $60 \times 80 =$ _____ $30 \times 900 =$ _____	**c.** $400 \times 50 =$ _____ $200 \times 200 =$ _____
d. $80 \times 800 =$ _____ $200 \times 500 =$ _____	**e.** $100 \times 100 =$ _____ $40 \times 30 =$ _____	**f.** $800 \times 300 =$ _____ $90 \times 1100 =$ _____

Write a number sentence for each question.

9. One hour has _____ minutes.

   How many minutes are in 12 hours? _____

   How many minutes are in 24 hours? _____

10. One hour has _____ minutes, and one minute has _____ seconds.

    How many seconds are there in one hour? _____

11. Ed earns $30 per hour.

    a. How much will he earn in an 8-hour workday? _____

    b. How much will he earn in a 40-hour workweek? _____

    c. How many days will he need to work in order to earn more than $1,000?

    _____

12. Find the missing factor. Think "backwards": how many zeros do you need?

a. _____ × 3 = 360	**b.** 40 × _____ = 320	**c.** _____ × 40 = 400
_____ × 50 = 450	5 × _____ = 600	_____ × 2 = 180
d. _____ × 30 = 4,800	**e.** 40 × _____ = 2,000	**f.** _____ × 800 = 56,000
_____ × 200 = 1,800	6 × _____ = 4,200	_____ × 20 = 12,000

Puzzle Corner   John wanted to prove that 40 × 70 is indeed 2,800 by breaking the multiplication into smaller parts. He wrote 40 as 4 × 10 and 70 as 7 × 10, and then multiplied in a different order:

$$40 \times 70 = 4 \times 10 \times 7 \times 10$$
$$= 10 \times 10 \times (4 \times 7) = 100 \times 28 = 2,800.$$

Do the same, and prove that 600 × 50 is indeed 30,000.

Multiply in Parts 1

Example 1. To multiply 3 × 46, break 46 into two parts: 40 and 6.

Then multiply those two parts separately by 3:
3 × 40 is 120, and 3 × 6 is 18.

Lastly add these two partial results: 120 + 18 = 138.

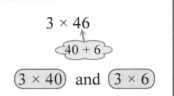

Example 2. This illustration shows the same thing, 3 × 46, using bundles of ten.

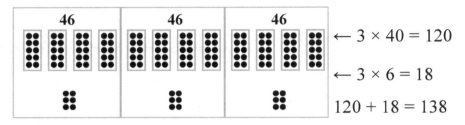

← 3 × 40 = 120

← 3 × 6 = 18

120 + 18 = 138

Study these examples. Multiply the tens and ones separately, then add:

8 × 13	**5 × 24**	**7 × 68**
(10 + 3)	(20 + 4)	(60 + 8)
8 × 10 and 8 × 3	5 × 20 and 5 × 4	7 × 60 and 7 × 8
80 and 24	100 and 20	420 and 56
= 104	= 120	= 476

1. Multiply the tens and ones separately. Then add to get the final answer.

a. 6 × 27	**b. 5 × 83**	**c. 9 × 34**
(20 + 7)	(+)	(+)
6 × _____ and 6 × ____	5 × _____ and 5 × ____	9 × _____ and 9 × ____
_____ and _____	_____ and _____	_____ and _____
= _____	= _____	= _____
d. 3 × 99	**e. 7 × 65**	**f. 4 × 58**
3 × _____ and 3 × ____	7 × _____ and 7 × ____	4 × _____ and 4 × ____
_____ and _____	_____ and _____	_____ and _____
= _____	= _____	= _____

Example 3. The picture shows the area of a rectangle with sides 8 and 24. It is also divided into two rectangles.

The area of the WHOLE rectangle is 8 × 24 square units. We can find 8 × 24 by calculating the areas of the *two* rectangles, and adding.

The area of the <u>first</u> rectangle is 8 × 20 = 160 square units. The area of the <u>second</u> rectangle is 8 × 4 = 32 square units.

Then, the area of the whole rectangle is the sum 160 + 32 = 192 square units.

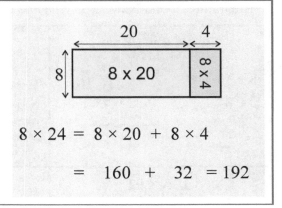

$$8 \times 24 = 8 \times 20 + 8 \times 4$$
$$= 160 + 32 = 192$$

2. Fill in the missing numbers. Write the area of the *whole* rectangle as a SUM of the areas of the *smaller* rectangles. Also find the total area.

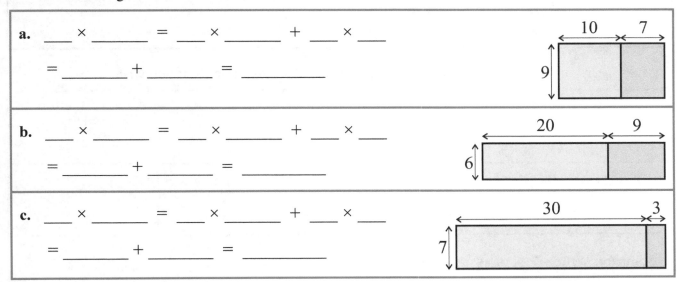

a. ___ × _____ = ___ × _____ + ___ × ___

= _____ + _____ = _____

b. ___ × _____ = ___ × _____ + ___ × ___

= _____ + _____ = _____

c. ___ × _____ = ___ × _____ + ___ × ___

= _____ + _____ = _____

3. It is your turn to draw. Draw a two-part rectangle to illustrate the multiplications, like in the previous problem. You don't have to draw accurately; a sketch is good enough.

a. 7 × 16 = ___ × _____ + ___ × ___

=

b. 5 × 21 = ___ × _____ + ___ × ___

=

c. 8 × 34 = ___ × _____ + ___ × ___

=

4. Break the second factor into tens and ones. Multiply separately, and add.

a. 6 × 19	b. 3 × 73	c. 4 × 67

$6 \times 10 \rightarrow$ 6 0
 $6 \times 9 \rightarrow$ + 5 4
             1 1 4
	$3 \times$ _____ $\rightarrow$
	 $3 \times$ _____ $\rightarrow$ +
	          _____	

d. 5 × 92	e. 9 × 33	f. 7 × 47

5. Multiply in parts. You can write the partial products under the problems, if you wish.

a. 5 × 13 = _____	b. 9 × 15 = _____	c. 5 × 33 = _____
d. 8 × 21 = _____	e. 4 × 22 = _____	f. 7 × 51 = _____

6. Compare. Write < , > , or = in the boxes.

    a.   10 × 10 ☐ 9 × 11   **b.**   6 × 12 ☐ 5 × 14   **c.**   8 × 22 ☐ 5 × 27

7. Solve. Write a number sentence for each problem, *not* just the answer.

a. Jack bought eight shirts for $14 each. What was the total cost?

_____

b. Mary and Harry set up nine rows of seats in the school auditorium, with 14 seats in each row. After that, they still had 56 seats left in the storage that they didn't use. How many seats are there in total?

_____

c. A small hammer costs $17. Another, much better one, costs three times as much. Find the cost of the more expensive hammer.

_____

Multiply in Parts 2

Multiplying in parts (partial products) works with larger numbers, too:

7 × 329

300 + 20 + 9

(7 × 300) and (7 × 20) and (7 × 9)

7 × 300 is 2,100. 7 × 20 is 140.
7 × 9 = 63.

Lastly, add the
partial results:

```
    2 1 0 0
      1 4 0
  +     6 3
  ─────────
    2,3 0 3
```

5 × 2,395

2,000 + 300 + 90 + 5

(5 × 2,000) + (5 × 300) + (5 × 90) + (5 × 5)

5 × 2,000 is 10,000. 5 × 300 is 1,500.
5 × 90 is 450. And 5 × 5 is 25.

Lastly, add the
partial results:

```
   1 0 0 0 0
     1 5 0 0
       4 5 0
   +     2 5
   ──────────
   1 1,9 7 5
```

1. Multiply in parts. Then add to get the final answer. Use the grids for additions.

a. 3 × 127
(100 + 20 + 7)

3 × _____ and 3 × _____ and 3 × _____

_____ and _____ and _____

= _____

b. 5 × 243
(   )

5 × _____ and 5 × _____ and 5 × _____

_____ and _____ and _____

= _____

c. 4 × 6,507
(   )

4 × _____ + 4 × _____ + 4 × _____

_____ + _____ + _____

= _____

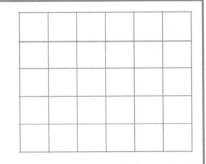

d. 5 × 4,813

5 × _____ + 5 × _____ + 5 × 10 + 5 × ___

_____ + _____ + _____ + _____

= _____

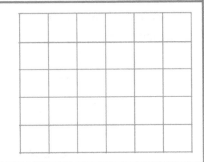

2. Break the second factor into thousands, hundreds, tens, and ones. Multiply separately, and add.

a. 4 × 128	**b. 8 × 151**	**c. 3 × 452**
$4 \times 100 \rightarrow$ 4 0 0 $4 \times 20 \rightarrow$ 8 0 $4 \times 8 \rightarrow$ + 3 2	+	+
d. 6 × 3,217	**e. 8 × 2,552**	**f. 6 × 1,098**
+	+	+

3. Solve. Write a number sentence for each problem, *not* just the answer.

a. Dad pays $138 in rent each month. How much does he pay in rent in half a year?

_____

_____

b. Find the perimeter of a square with 255 cm sides.

_____

_____

c. One roll contains 56 cm of material, and another roll contains five times as much. Find how much material both rolls contain in total.

_____

_____

Multiply in Parts – Area Model

1. Write the area of the *whole* rectangle as a SUM of the areas of the *smaller* rectangles. Also find the total area. Use the grid for the final addition.

a.

8×127

= $8 \times$ _____ + $8 \times$ _____ + $8 \times$ _____

The total area is _____ square units.

b.

___ $\times$ _____

= ___ $\times$ _____ + ___ $\times$ _____ + ___ $\times$ _____

The total area is _____ square units.

c.

___ $\times$ _____

= ___ $\times$ _____ + ___ $\times$ _____ + ___ $\times$ _____

The total area is _____ square units.

Remember? The expressions (number sentences) on the left and right sides of the "=" sign have *an equal value*:	$2 \times 6 = 3 \times 4$	$18 - 3 = 5 \times 3$
	$12 = 12$	$15 = 15$

2. Fill in the missing numbers to make the expressions equal.

a. $6 \times 6 = 9 \times$ _____

b. _____ $\times 10 = 5 \times 24$

c. $20 +$ _____ $= 4 \times 10$

d. $6000 = 30 \times$ _____

e. $120 - 75 = 5 \times$ _____

f. _____ $+ 750 = 5 \times 300$

103

3. It is your turn to draw. Draw a *three*-part rectangle to illustrate the multiplications, as in the previous problems. You don't have to draw accurately; a sketch is good enough. Find the area of each part and the total area. Use the grids for the additions.

a. 7×153

Areas of the parts:

Total area:

b. 5×218

Areas of the parts:

Total area:

c. 8×376

Areas of the parts:

Total area:

4. Solve. Write number sentence(s) on the empty lines to show your work.

a. Susie orders roses for her flower shop in bunches of six dozen (72 flowers) at a time. She places an order once a week. How many roses will Susie order in total for five weeks?

_____

_____

b. One bunch of six dozen roses costs her $70. What is the total cost for five weeks of orders for roses?

_____

_____

Multiplying Money Amounts

We can also multiply in parts with money amounts.		
3 × $1.70 Think of $1.70 as $1 and 70¢. Multiply separately: 3 × $1 is $3.00. 3 × 70¢ is 210¢ or $2.10. Lastly add: $3.00 + $2.10 = $5.10.	**8 × $4.28** Multiply in parts: 8 × $4 is $32. Next, 8 × 20¢ is 160¢ or $1.60. Then, 8 × 8¢ is 64¢. Lastly add (on the right).	$32.00 $0.64 + $1.60 ————— $34.24

1. Multiply in parts, and lastly add.

a. 6 × $11.85 6 × $11 → 6 × $0.80 → 6 × $0.05 → + _____	**b. 5 × $2.93** + _____
c. 7 × $3.75 + _____	**d. 8 × $10.95** + _____

2. Break the money amounts into dollars and cents. Multiply separately, and lastly add.

a. 6 × $2.80 _____ + _____ = (6 × $2) (6 × $0.80)	**b. 5 × $4.70** _____ + _____ = (5 × $4) (5 × $0.70)
c. 4 × $12.50	**d. 7 × $5.61**

3. **a.** Sandra bought five books for $2.70 each. What was the total cost?

   b. She paid with $20. What was her change?

4. **a.** A ticket to a concert costs $23.50. What is the total cost for tickets for a family of four?

   b. What is their change from $100?

5. Continue the patterns according to the instructions.

a. Start at 80. Add 40 each time:	**b.** Start at 42,000. Subtract 3,000 each time:	**c.** Start at 1. Add 5 each time:
_1 2 0_	_____	_____
_____	_____	_____
_____	_____	_____
_____	_____	_____
_____	_____	_____
_____	_____	_____
_____	_____	_____
What does this pattern remind you of?	What does this pattern remind you of?	_____
		_____

6. Notice the pattern of odd and even numbers in part (c). Can you explain why this happens?

Estimating in Multiplication

If you don't need an exact result, you can estimate. To estimate the result of a multiplication, round some or all of the factors so that you can easily multiply *mentally*.

Estimate 8 × 189.	**Estimate 42 × 78.**	**Estimate 21 × $4.52.**
189 can be rounded to 200. The estimated product is 8 × 200 = 1,600.	42 ≈ 40 and 78 ≈ 80. The estimated product is 40 × 80 = 3,200.	First round the numbers to 20 and $4.50. Then, since 2 × $4.50 is nine dollars, 20 × $4.50 is ten times that, or $90.

1. Estimate the results by rounding one or both factors. Don't round both numbers if you can multiply in your head just by rounding one factor.

a. 5 × 69 ≈ _____ × _____ = _____	**b.** 11 × 58 ≈ _____ × _____ = _____	**c.** 119 × 8 ≈ _____ × _____ = _____
d. 27 × 52 ≈ _____ × _____ = _____	**e.** 7 × $4.15 ≈ _____ × _____ = _____	**f.** 8 × $11.79 ≈ _____ × _____ = _____
g. 25 × $42.50 ≈ _____ × _____ = _____	**h.** 9 × 17 ≈ _____ × _____ = _____	**i.** 63 × 897 ≈ _____ × _____ = _____

2. Estimate the total cost. Round one or both numbers so that you can multiply in your head. Write a number sentence to show your multiplication with rounded numbers.

a. 24 chairs at $44.95 per chair	**b.** 512 Popsicles at 19¢ each
c. 210 meters of wire at $1.49 per meter	**d.** Six tennis balls that cost $3.37 each and two rackets that cost $11.90 each.

Example. If each bus can seat 57 passengers, how many buses do you need to seat 450 people?

Let's think:

> One bus seats 57 passengers.   Ten buses seat 570 passengers.
> Two buses seat 114 passengers.   Eight buses seat 8 × 57 passengers.   *Etc.*

So how many buses will we need for our answer to be 450 or a little more?

This problem could be solved by division (450 ÷ 57), but it is easier to **use estimation and multiplication**. Round 57 to 60, and quickly calculate in your head this way:

7 × 60 = 420 and 8 × 60 = 480. It *looks like* 8 buses are needed for 450 people.

Lastly, let's check our answer using the exact number 57:
8 × 57 = 400 + 56 = 456, so yes, eight buses are enough to transport 450 people.

3. Solve the problems using estimation.

a. An advertisement in a newspaper costs $349.
How many ads can Bill buy with $2,000?

b. It costs $2.85 per hour to skate at a skating rink. Sandra
has $25. How many whole hours can she afford to skate?

c. A can of beans costs $0.29. A bag of lentils costs $0.42.
Estimate which is cheaper: to buy eight cans of beans
or to buy five bags of lentils.

d. Jackie needs to buy 8 feet of string for each of
the 28 students in the craft class.
The string costs $0.22 per foot. Estimate the total cost.

Multiply in Columns—the Easy Way

```
    3 8              3 8              3 8              3 8
  ×   6            ×   6            ×   6            ×   6
  _____          _____          _____          _____
                      4 8              4 8              4 8
                                    1 8 0          + 1 8 0
                                                   _____
                                                     2 2 8
```

Let's multiply 6 × 38 in parts, writing one number under the other.

First multiply 6 × 8.

Then multiply 6 × 30 and write the result under the 48. Remember, the "3" is in the tens place in the number 38 so it actually means 30.

Lastly, add.

Multiply 9 × 2.	Then 9 × 80.	Add.	Multiply 3 × 7.	Then 3 × 40.	Add.

```
    8 2           8 2            8 2          4 7          4 7          4 7
  ×   9         ×   9          ×   9        ×   3        ×   3        ×   3
  _____       _____        _____      _____      _____      _____
    1 8           1 8            1 8          2 1          2 1          2 1
                7 2 0        + 7 2 0                    1 2 0        + 1 2 0
                             _____                                 _____
                               7 3 8                                   1 4 1
```

1. Multiply.

a.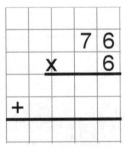

b.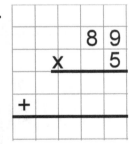

c.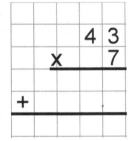

d.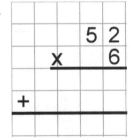

e.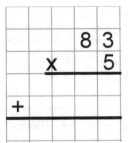

f.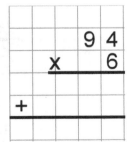

g.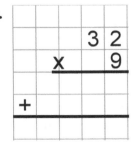

h.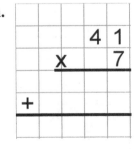

Multiplying a 3-digit number happens in exactly the same way.	ones: 7×6	tens: 7×20	hundreds: 7×500	Add.
You multiply in parts: first the ones, then the tens, then the hundreds. Lastly, add.	5 2 **6** × **7** ——— **4 2**	5 **2** 6 × **7** ——— 4 2 **1 4 0**	**5** 2 6 × **7** ——— 4 2 1 4 0 **3 5 0 0**	5 2 6 × 7 ——— 4 2 1 4 0 + 3 5 0 0 ——— 3 6 8 2
Just don't forget that you are multiplying *whole tens* and *whole hundreds*, not just "plain" numbers.				

2. Multiply.

a. 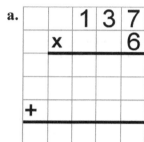   b. 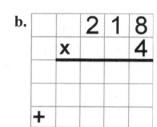   c. 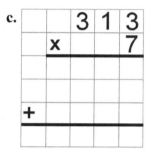   d.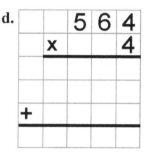

e. 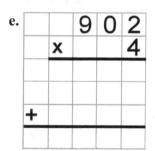   f. 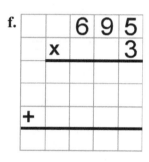   g. 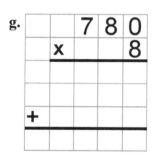   h.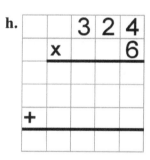

i.   j. 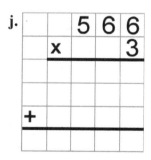   k. 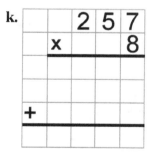   l.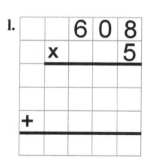

3. Solve the equations.

a. $\triangle \times 80 = 480$ $\triangle = \underline{\hspace{2cm}}$	**b.** $5 \times \underline{\ ?\ } = 450$ $\underline{\ ?\ } = \underline{\hspace{2cm}}$	**c.** $900 \times z = 81{,}000$ $z = \underline{\hspace{2cm}}$

4. Solve.   **a.** $58 \times 5 + 291$ **b.** $1,000 - 3 \times 145$

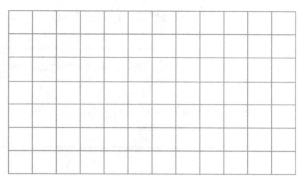

5. Solve.

a. A \$236 burglar alarm is discounted by \$40. A store buys seven. What is the total cost?

b. One side of a square is 248 feet. What is its perimeter?

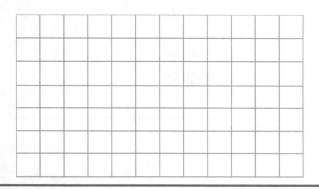 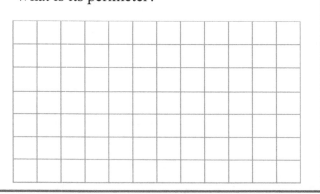

6. Solve the equations.

a. $50 \times \underline{\ ?\ } = 2,000$

$\underline{\ ?\ } = \underline{\hspace{2cm}}$

b. $\triangle \times 60 = 2,400$

$\triangle = \underline{\hspace{2cm}}$

c. $70 \times z = 49,000$

$z = \underline{\hspace{2cm}}$

d. $\triangle \times 30 = 9 \times 40$

$\triangle = \underline{\hspace{2cm}}$

e. $5 \times \underline{\ ?\ } \times 2 = 1,000$

$\underline{\ ?\ } = \underline{\hspace{2cm}}$

f. $40 \times p = 800 \times 4$

$p = \underline{\hspace{2cm}}$

Figure out the missing numbers.

a.
```
    ☐ ☐ ☐
  ×       7
  ─────────
        1 4
      4 9 0
  +   7 0 0
  ─────────
```

b.
```
    ☐ ☐ ☐
  ×       4
  ─────────
      ☐ ☐
      2 0 0
  + 1 2 0 0
  ─────────
    1 4 3 2
```

c.
```
    ☐ ☐ ☐
  ×       9
  ─────────
        8 1
      ☐ ☐
  + 6 3 0 0
  ─────────
    6 3 8 1
```

Multiply in Columns—the Easy Way, Part 2

Multiplying a 4-digit number is done in exactly the same way. You multiply in parts: first the ones, then the tens, then the hundreds, and then the thousands. Lastly, add.

Remember that you are multiplying *whole tens, whole hundreds,* and *whole thousands*—not just "plain" numbers.

ones:	tens:	hundreds:	thousands:	Add.
7 × 8	7 × 70	7 × 400	7 × 2,000	

```
    ones:            tens:            hundreds:        thousands:            Add.
    7 × 8            7 × 70           7 × 400          7 × 2,000

    2 4 7 8          2 4 7 8          2 4 7 8          2 4 7 8            2 4 7 8
  ×       7        ×       7        ×       7        ×       7          ×       7
  ─────────        ─────────        ─────────        ─────────         ─────────
      5 6              5 6              5 6              5 6                 5 6
                     4 9 0            4 9 0            4 9 0               4 9 0
                                    2 8 0 0          2 8 0 0             2 8 0 0
                                                   1 4 0 0 0         + 1 4 0 0 0
                                                                      ─────────
                                                                     1 7 3 4 6
```

1. Multiply.

a.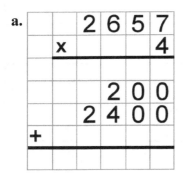

b.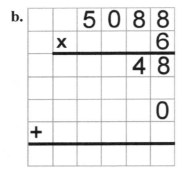

c. (8106 × 3)

d.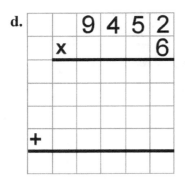

e.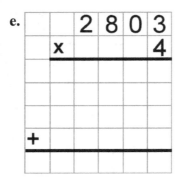

f.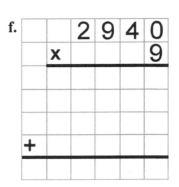

112

2. Multiply.

a.   5 × 1,986

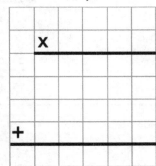

b.   9 × 2,055

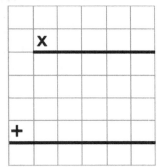

c.   7 × 3,280

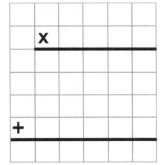

d.   6 × 6,117

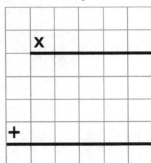

e.   5 × 2,489

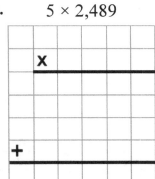

f.   8 × 4,301

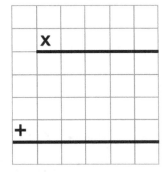

3. Solve. Write a number sentence or several for each problem.

a. The distance from Greg's house to his friend Jamie's house is 3,820 feet. What distance does Greg walk if he goes from his home to Jamie's and back *twice*?

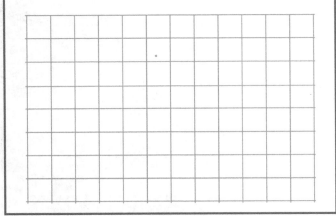

b. Jennie has 55 marbles and Sue has four times as many. How many marbles do the girls have together?

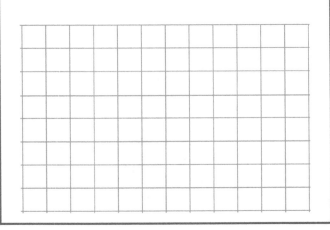

You can also multiply money amounts in parts.		$ 5 . 1 8 × 4		$ 2 3 . 5 7 × 3
Multiply first the individual cents, then the ten-cent amounts, and then the whole dollars.	4 × 0.08 (cents) → 4 × 0.10 (ten-cents) → 4 × $5 (dollars) →	0 . 3 2 0 . 4 0 + 2 0 . 0 0 $ 2 0 . 7 2	3 × 0.07 → 3 × 0.50 → 3 × $23 →	0 . 2 1 1 . 5 0 + 6 9 . 0 0 $ 7 0 . 7 1

4. Multiply.

a.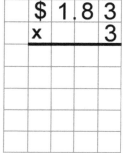

b.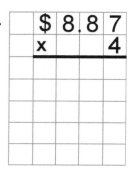

c.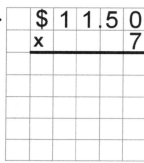

d.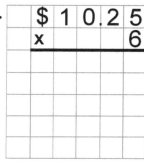

e.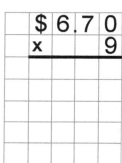

f.

g.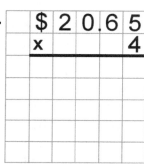

h. $ 5 3 . 0 8   × 6

5. Solve. Write a number sentence to show your estimation on the empty line.

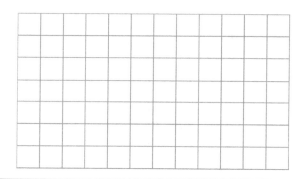

a. You bought nine notebooks for $1.57 each. What was the total cost?

Estimate: _____

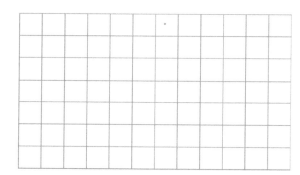

b. How much is your change, if you buy eight sandwiches for $2.28 each, and pay with $20?

Estimate: _____

Multiplying in Columns, the Standard Way

The standard algorithm of multiplication is based on a principle you already know: multiplying in parts (partial products). We simply multiply ones, tens, and hundreds of the number separately, and then add.

However, in the standard algorithm, the additions are done *at the same time* as the multiplications—not afterwards. That way, the calculation looks more compact and takes less space.

The standard way to multiply		"The easy way"
$$\begin{array}{r} {}^{1} \\ 6\ 3 \\ \times\ \ \ 4 \\ \hline 2 \end{array}$$ Multiply the ones: $4 \times 3 = 12$. Place 2 in the ones place, but write the tens digit (1) above the tens column as a little memory note. You are *regrouping* (carrying).	$$\begin{array}{r} {}^{1} \\ 6\ 3 \\ \times\ \ \ 4 \\ \hline 2\ 5\ 2 \end{array}$$ Then multiply the tens, *adding* the 1 ten that was regrouped: $$4 \times 6 + 1 = 25$$ Write 25 in front of the 2. <u>Note:</u> This 25 means 25 tens or 250!	$$\begin{array}{r} 6\ 3 \\ \times\ \ \ 4 \\ \hline 1\ 2 \\ +\ 2\ 4\ 0 \\ \hline 2\ 5\ 2 \end{array}$$ In the "easy way," we multiply in parts, and the adding is done separately.

The standard way to multiply		"The easy way"
$$\begin{array}{r} {}^{3} \\ 7\ 5 \\ \times\ \ \ 7 \\ \hline 5 \end{array}$$ Multiply the ones: $7 \times 5 = 35$ Regroup the 3 tens.	$$\begin{array}{r} {}^{3} \\ 7\ 5 \\ \times\ \ \ 7 \\ \hline 5\ 2\ 5 \end{array}$$ Multiply & add the tens: $7 \times 7 + 3 = 52$	$$\begin{array}{r} 7\ 5 \\ \times\ \ \ 7 \\ \hline 3\ 5 \\ +\ 4\ 9\ 0 \\ \hline 5\ 2\ 5 \end{array}$$

1. Multiply using both methods: the standard way and the easy way.

a.

$$\begin{array}{r} 5\ 3 \\ \times\ \ \ 8 \\ \hline \end{array} \qquad \begin{array}{r} 5\ 3 \\ \times\ \ \ 8 \\ \hline \end{array}$$

b.

$$\begin{array}{r} 8\ 8 \\ \times\ \ \ 3 \\ \hline \end{array} \qquad \begin{array}{r} 8\ 8 \\ \times\ \ \ 3 \\ \hline \end{array}$$

2. Multiply using both methods: the standard way and the easy way.

a.

```
      7 9
  x     3
```

```
      7 9
  x     3
  _____
```

b.

```
      1 8
  x     5
  _____
```

```
      1 8
  x     5
  _____
```

3. Multiply. Be careful with the regrouping.

a.

```
      5 1
  x     6
```

b.

```
      1 9
  x     3
```

c.

```
      6 2
  x     2
```

d.

```
      4 6
  x     7
```

e.

```
      6 6
  x     6
```

f.

```
      3 9
  x     9
```

g.

```
      8 7
  x     3
```

h.

```
      6 7
  x     2
```

i.

```
      2 0
  x     9
```

j.

```
      5 4
  x     8
```

k.

```
      3 4
  x     6
```

l.

```
      4 6
  x     2
```

4. Write number sentences (additions, subtractions, multiplications) on the lines, and solve.

a. What is the cost of buying three chairs for $48 each?

_____

And the cost for six chairs? _____

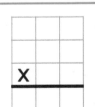

b. You earn $77 a day. How much do you earn in five days?

_____

How much in ten days? _____

With a 3- or 4-digit number you have to regroup several times.

$$\begin{array}{r} \overset{3}{} \\ 2\ 3\ \mathbf{8} \\ \times\quad \mathbf{4} \\ \hline \mathbf{2} \end{array}$$

Multiply the ones first.

$$4 \times 8 = 32$$

Write 2 in the ones place and regroup the 3 tens to the tens column.

$$\begin{array}{r} \overset{1}{}\overset{3}{} \\ 2\ \mathbf{3}\ 8 \\ \times\quad \mathbf{4} \\ \hline \mathbf{5}\ 2 \end{array}$$

Then multiply the tens, adding the 3 regrouped tens:

$$4 \times 3 + 3 = 15$$

Write 5 in the tens place and regroup the 1 hundred.

$$\begin{array}{r} \overset{1}{}\overset{3}{} \\ \mathbf{2}\ 3\ 8 \\ \times\quad \mathbf{4} \\ \hline \mathbf{9}\ 5\ 2 \end{array}$$

Then multiply the hundreds, adding the regrouped hundred:

$$4 \times 2 + 1 = 9$$

Write 9 in the hundreds place.

$$\begin{array}{r} \overset{1}{} \\ 7\ 6\ 5\ \mathbf{2} \\ \times\quad\quad \mathbf{5} \\ \hline \mathbf{0} \end{array}$$

Multiply the ones:

$$5 \times 2 = 10$$

Write 0 in the ones place and regroup the 1 ten.

$$\begin{array}{r} \overset{2}{}\overset{1}{} \\ 7\ 6\ \mathbf{5}\ 2 \\ \times\quad\quad \mathbf{5} \\ \hline \mathbf{6}\ 0 \end{array}$$

Then the tens. Add the regrouped ten:

$$5 \times 5 + 1 = 26$$

Write 6 in the tens place and regroup the 2 hundreds.

$$\begin{array}{r} \overset{3}{}\overset{2}{}\overset{1}{} \\ 7\ \mathbf{6}\ 5\ 2 \\ \times\quad\quad \mathbf{5} \\ \hline \mathbf{2}\ 6\ 0 \end{array}$$

Multiply the hundreds:

$$5 \times 6 + 2 = 32$$

Write 2 in the hundreds place, and regroup the 3 thousands.

$$\begin{array}{r} \overset{3}{}\overset{2}{}\overset{1}{} \\ \mathbf{7}\ 6\ 5\ 2 \\ \times\quad\quad \mathbf{5} \\ \hline 3\ 8\ 2\ 6\ 0 \end{array}$$

Multiply the thousands:

$$5 \times 7 + 3 = 38$$

Write 38 in front of the 260.

5. Multiply using both methods: the standard way and the easy way.

a.

$$\begin{array}{r} 1\ 2\ 3 \\ \times\quad 8 \\ \hline \end{array}$$

$$\begin{array}{r} 1\ 2\ 3 \\ \times\quad 8 \\ \hline \end{array}$$

b.

$$\begin{array}{r} 2\ 7\ 9 \\ \times\quad 3 \\ \hline \end{array}$$

$$\begin{array}{r} 2\ 7\ 9 \\ \times\quad 3 \\ \hline \end{array}$$

c.

$$\begin{array}{r} 4\ 6\ 3 \\ \times\quad 5 \\ \hline \end{array}$$

$$\begin{array}{r} 4\ 6\ 3 \\ \times\quad 5 \\ \hline \end{array}$$

d.

$$\begin{array}{r} 1\ 5\ 6 \\ \times\quad 6 \\ \hline \end{array}$$

$$\begin{array}{r} 1\ 5\ 6 \\ \times\quad 6 \\ \hline \end{array}$$

6. Multiply using the standard method.

a.	b.	c.	d.
4 6 2 × 2	5 0 6 × 7	2 7 8 × 5	3 1 9 × 7
e.	**f.**	**g.**	**h.**
2 8 8 × 3	8 0 9 × 9	2 8 7 × 3	3 6 7 × 2
i.	**j.**	**k.**	**l.**
1 2 0 8 × 9	2 5 1 4 × 3	6 1 7 7 × 4	5 3 3 0 × 9

7. Find the perimeter and area of a rectangular room that measures 9 ft by 28 ft.

_____

_____

8. Find what errors these children make.

a. Figure out what error Minnie makes every time she multiplies.

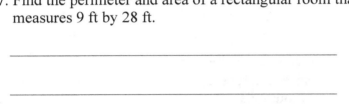

```
   4                    2                  4 2
   7 8                  3 8                1 3 3
 ×   3                ×   9              ×     4
 ─────                ─────              ───────
 2 5 2                2 9 7              8 1 1
```

b. This is Andy's math work. Where does he go wrong?

```
   2 8                  4 5                2 1 5
 ×   3                ×   5              ×     3
 ─────                ─────              ───────
 6 2 4                2 0 2 5            6 3 1 5
```

118

Multiplying in Columns, Practice

Estimate the answer before calculating. If the estimated answer is very different from the calculated answer, there could be an error.

Estimation: $5 \times 45 \approx 5 \times 50 = 250$ The estimated answer 250 is VERY different from the calculated answer 2025. There must be an error! Can you find it and correct it?	$\begin{array}{r} 4\ 5 \\ \times\ \ \ \ 5 \\ \hline 2\ 0\ 2\ 5 \end{array}$
Estimation: $7 \times 418 \approx 7 \times 400 = 2,800$ The estimation (2,800) and the calculated answer (2,926) are fairly close. This does *not* prove the answer is correct, but if there is an error, it is a "smaller" one.	$\begin{array}{r} {\scriptstyle 1\ 5} \\ 4\ 1\ 8 \\ \times\ \ \ \ \ \ 7 \\ \hline 2\ 9\ 2\ 6 \end{array}$

1. First, estimate the answer. Then multiply to find the exact result.

a. Estimate: $\approx \underline{\ 9\ } \times \underline{\ 40\ } = \underline{\ 360\ }$	$\begin{array}{r} 4\ 3 \\ \times\ \ \ \ 9 \\ \hline \end{array}$
b. Estimate: $\approx \underline{\ \ \ } \times \underline{\ \ \ \ \ \ } = \underline{\ \ \ \ \ \ }$	$\begin{array}{r} 7\ 2 \\ \times\ \ \ \ 8 \\ \hline \end{array}$
c. Estimate: $\approx$	$\begin{array}{r} 7\ 7\ 1 \\ \times\ \ \ \ \ \ 3 \\ \hline \end{array}$
d. Estimate: $\approx \underline{\ \ \ } \times \underline{\ \ \ \ \ \ } = \underline{\ \ \ \ \ \ }$	$\begin{array}{r} 8\ 1\ 9 \\ \times\ \ \ \ \ \ 5 \\ \hline \end{array}$
e. Estimate: $\approx$	$\begin{array}{r} 2\ 5\ 2\ 1 \\ \times\ \ \ \ \ \ \ \ 4 \\ \hline \end{array}$
f. Estimate: $\approx$	$\begin{array}{r} 8\ 7\ 1\ 2 \\ \times\ \ \ \ \ \ \ \ 3 \\ \hline \end{array}$

2. A first grade math book has 187 pages, and an eighth grade math book is three times as long. How many pages does it have?

_____

_____

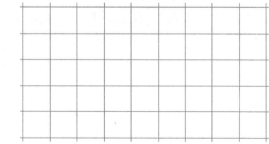

119

3. Solve. Write number sentence(s) to show your calculation(s).
One package of paper contains 250 sheets. Marie needed
1,300 sheets. How many packages did she need to buy?

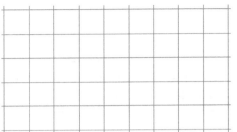

_____

_____

4. A school with 304 students hired buses to take the students to
a museum. Each bus could seat 43 passengers.

a. How many students could four buses seat?

b. How many students could seven buses seat?

c. How many buses do they need for all 304 students?

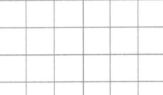

5. Solve the equations.

a.	b.	c.
$70 \times \triangle = 5{,}600$	$60 \times \underline{\ ?\ } = 2 \times 90$	$5 \times 2 \times y = 300$
$\triangle = \underline{\hspace{2cm}}$	$\underline{\ ?\ } = \underline{\hspace{2cm}}$	$y = \underline{\hspace{2cm}}$

6. Let your teacher decide if you need more practice. Multiply. Estimate the answer on the line.

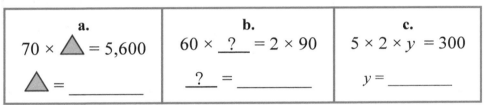

a. 5×196	**b.** 9×205	**c.** $9 \times 9{,}807$	**d.** $6 \times 4{,}810$
$\approx$ _____	$\approx$ _____	$\approx$ _____	$\approx$ _____

Puzzle Corner   Find the missing numbers in these multiplications:

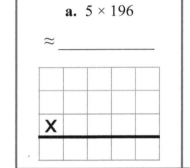
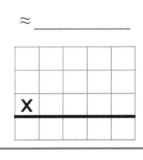
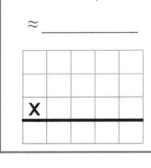
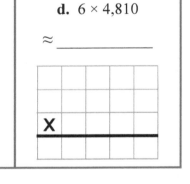

Order of Operations Again

1. Calculate anything within parentheses ( ).	$20 - 2 \times 5 + 9$ $(20 - 2) \times 5 + 9$
2. Do multiplications and divisions from left to right.	$= 20 - 10 + 9$ $= 18 \times 5 + 9$
3. Do additions and subtractions from left to right.	$= 10 + 9 = 19$ $= 90 + 9 = 99$

1. The following calculation has five operations. In which order are they done?

$$650 - 9 \times (23 + 31) + 211$$

a. First calculate the sum _____ + _____.

b. Next multiply that sum by _____.

c. Subtract that result from _____.

d. Lastly add _____ to the subtraction result.

2. Multiply in any order. Try to find the easiest order.

a.	b.	c.	d.
$2 \times 3 \times 300 =$	$6 \times 5 \times 7 =$	$40 \times 10 \times 8 =$	$20 \times 70 \times 2 =$
$10 \times 5 \times 3 =$	$5 \times 8 \times 50 =$	$10 \times 0 \times 40 =$	$70 \times 4 \times 20 =$

3. Solve and compare the problems in each box.

a.	b.	c.
$500 - 2 \times 200 =$ _____	$70 \times (30 + 20) =$ _____	$(500 - 200) \times 2 =$ _____
$500 + 2 \times 200 =$ _____	$70 \times (30 - 20) =$ _____	$(500 + 200) \times 2 =$ _____

4. Solve.

a. $70 \times 30 - 2{,}000 =$ _____	**b.** $8 \times 200 - 200 - 500 =$ _____
c. $10 \times 7 \times (50 + 30) + 200 =$ _____	**d.** $90 + (15 + 5) \times 7 =$ _____
e. $800 - 2 \times 20 + 100 =$ _____	**f.** $(500 - 50 - 50) \times 7 - 100 =$ _____

5. Calculate in the right order.

a. $5 \times 98 - 2 \times 87$

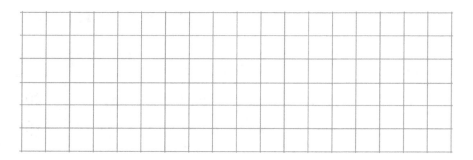

b. $2{,}819 - 4 \times (28 + 138)$

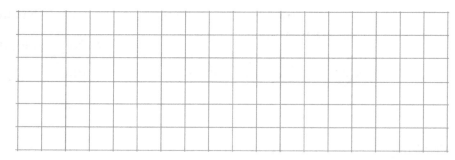

c. $8 \times (281 - 133) - 4 \times 15$

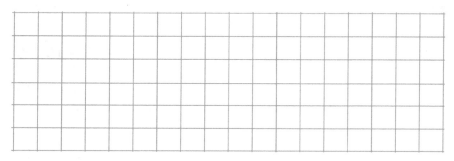

6. Find a matching number sentence for each problem, and solve.

a. Lisa bought four cards for $2 each and three shirts for $3 each. What was the total cost?

b. Mom bought crayons for $2 and a book for $3 for each of the four children. What was the total cost?

c. Mark bought five packs of paper clips for $3 each and five pens for $2 each. What was his change from $50?

$4 \times (\$2 + \$3)$

$4 \times \$2 + 3 \times \$3$

$4 \times \$3 + \$2$

$4 \times \$3 \times 2$

$\$50 - 5 \times \$3 + \$2$

$\$50 - 5 \times \$3 \times 2$

$\$50 - 5 \times \$3 - 5 \times \$2$

7. Solve for the unknown N.

a. $3 \times N \times 3 = 27$ N = _____	**b.** $N \times 2 \times 100 = 2,400$ N = _____	**c.** $20 \times 3 \times N = 180$ N = _____
d. $N \div 5 = 300$ N = _____	**e.** $180 \div N = 20$ N = _____	**f.** $32 \div N = 16 \div 2$ N = _____

8. Write a number sentence or several for each problem and solve.

   a. Elisa bought seven flash drives for $25 each.
   What was her change from $200?

   _____

   _____

   b. What is the total weight of eight 3-kg bags of strawberries
   and fifteen 2-kg bags of blueberries?

   _____

   _____

   c. An apartment building is nine stories high, and each story
   is 9 feet tall. Another apartment building is three times as
   tall as that one. How tall is the second building?

   _____

   _____

   d. How much cheaper is it to buy nine cans of cat food for $3 each
   than to buy two boxes of cat food for $18 each?

   _____

   _____

Puzzle Corner   Put operation symbols $+$, $-$, or $\times$ into the boxes and add
parentheses ( ) so that the calculations become true.

   a. $7 \,\square\, 2 \,\square\, 8 = 70$ **b.** $80 \,\square\, 5 \,\square\, 10 \,\square\, 5 = 55$ **c.** $4 \,\square\, 8 \,\square\, 5 \,\square\, 20 = 40$

Money and Change

Multiplying money amounts is done the same way as multiplying whole numbers. Just remember that **the answer needs a decimal point and a dollar sign** ($). And first, estimate the result.	Estimation: $8 \times \$3.59$ $\approx 8 \times \$4 = \$32$	$\begin{array}{r} {\scriptstyle 4\ \ 7} \\ \$3.5\ 9 \\ \times\ \ \ \ \ \ \ 8 \\ \hline \$2\ 8.7\ 2 \end{array}$

1. Multiply money amounts. Estimate first.

a. Estimation: $\approx 4 \times \underline{\ 4.50\ } = \underline{\ \$18\ }$ $\begin{array}{r} \$4.5\ 5 \\ \times\ \ \ \ \ \ \ 4 \\ \hline \end{array}$	b. Estimation: $\approx \underline{\ \ \ \ } \times \underline{\ \ \ \ \ \ \ \ } = \underline{\ \ \ \ \ \ \ }$ $\begin{array}{r} \$9.7\ 0 \\ \times\ \ \ \ \ \ \ 4 \\ \hline \end{array}$	c. Estimation: $\approx \underline{\ \ \ \ } \times \underline{\ \ \ \ \ \ \ \ } = \underline{\ \ \ \ \ \ \ }$ $\begin{array}{r} \$4.9\ 1 \\ \times\ \ \ \ \ \ \ 7 \\ \hline \end{array}$
d. Estimation: $\approx \underline{\ \ \ \ } \times \underline{\ \ \ \ \ \ \ \ } = \underline{\ \ \ \ \ \ \ }$ $\begin{array}{r} \$0.8\ 2 \\ \times\ \ \ \ \ \ \ 6 \\ \hline \end{array}$	e. Estimation: $\approx \underline{\ \ \ \ } \times \underline{\ \ \ \ \ \ \ \ } = \underline{\ \ \ \ \ \ \ }$ $\begin{array}{r} \$1\ 2.5\ 3 \\ \times\ \ \ \ \ \ \ \ \ \ 7 \\ \hline \end{array}$	f. Estimation: $\approx \underline{\ \ \ \ } \times \underline{\ \ \ \ \ \ \ \ } = \underline{\ \ \ \ \ \ \ }$ $\begin{array}{r} \$4\ 3.1\ 5 \\ \times\ \ \ \ \ \ \ \ \ \ 5 \\ \hline \end{array}$

2. If you buy eight cans of fish for $1.39 each, what is your change from $20?

Estimation:

Calculations:

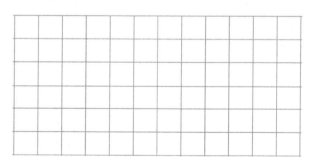

3. Fill in the missing parts in the bar models and in the number sentences. Solve.

a. Jill bought three baskets for $7.20 each. She paid with $50. What was her change (x)?

$$3 \times \$7.20 + x = \$50$$

$$x = \$\underline{\hspace{2cm}} - \underline{\hspace{1cm}} \times \$\underline{\hspace{1.5cm}}$$

b. James bought four wheels for $29 each, and afterwards he had $51 left. How much did he have originally (x)?

$$x = 4 \times \$\underline{\hspace{1.5cm}} + \$\underline{\hspace{1.5cm}}$$

c. Jack had $30. Then he bought five screwdrivers for $3.08 apiece. How much did he have left (x)?

$$5 \times \$\underline{\hspace{1.5cm}} + x = \$\underline{\hspace{1.5cm}}$$

$$x = \$\underline{\hspace{2cm}} - \underline{\hspace{1cm}} \times \$\underline{\hspace{1.5cm}}$$

d. Mom bought five meals for $11.50 per meal. Now she has $12.50 left. How much did she have originally (x)?

$$x = 5 \times \$\underline{\hspace{1.5cm}} + \$\underline{\hspace{1.5cm}}$$

125

4. A pack of four bottles of juice costs $2.76.
   You want 20 bottles. What is the total cost?

   My estimate:

   My calculations:

5. A teacher bought 20 pencils for $0.15 each
   and 10 notebooks for $1.09 each.
   What was the total cost?

   My estimate:

   My calculations:

6. Paul bought four computer mice for $9.80 each
   and a hard drive for $65, and had $25.80 left.
   How much money did Paul have initially?

   My estimate:

   My calculations:

Puzzle Corner
A construction company bought eight wheelbarrows. The wheelbarrows used to cost $145 but now they were discounted. The total bill came to exactly $1,000. How much was the discount for one wheelbarrow?

So Many of the Same Thing

1. Fill in the tables, thinking logically!

a. A bus is traveling at the speed of 45 miles per hour. That means it travels 45 miles in one hour. Fill in the table how many miles the bus travels in the given amount of hours.

Miles	45									
Hours	1	2	3	4	5	6	7	8	9	10

b. One meter of fabric costs $5.10. Fill in the table.

Dollars	$5.10									
Meters	1	2	3	4	5	6	7	8	9	10

c. Two cans of beans cost $3.00. Fill in the table.

Dollars		$3.00								
Cans	1	2	3	4	5	6	7	8	9	10

d. You can get four buckets of paint for $60. Fill in the table.

Dollars		$60								
Buckets	2	4	6	8	10	12	14	16	18	20

e. An earthworm can travel at the speed of 240 feet per hour. Notice that the table has minutes!

Feet										
Minutes	10	20	30	40	50	60	70	80	90	100

f. Ernie can patch four bicycle tires in an hour.

Tires	Minutes
1	
2	
3	
4	
5	
6	

g. Maria can knit three scarves in nine days.

Days	Scarves
3	
6	
9	
12	
15	
18	

h. Jack earned $75 in five hours.

Hours	Dollars
1	
2	
3	
4	
5	
6	

Two identical bags contain 12 kg of potatoes in total. How many such bags would you need to have 30 kg of potatoes? To solve this problem, you can make a chart like the one on the right:		
	1 bag	_____ kg
	2 bags	12 kg
	3 bags	3×6 kg $= 18$ kg
	_____ bags	_____ $\times 6$ kg $= 30$ kg

The total number of chocolates in five identical boxes was 30. How many chocolates would two boxes contain?	First find out how many are in ONE box:	
	1 box	_____ chocolates
	2 boxes	_____ chocolates
	5 boxes	30 chocolates

2. Solve the problems using the tables. First find out the answer for ONE of the things.

a. Six flowers cost $18. How much would five flowers cost?

1 flower	
5 flowers	
6 flowers	$18

b. Four cans of peas weigh 800 g. How much would three cans weigh?

4 cans	800 g

c. A package of three fishing lures costs $6. How much would seven lures cost?

3 lures	$6

d. Mark can watch three episodes of the "Animal Farm" series in 90 minutes. How long would it take for him to watch 5 episodes?

e. Mark did five sit-ups in ten seconds. How many could he do in one minute if he maintains the same speed?

f. Ten notebooks cost $20.
What would seven cost?

g. Ann read 120 pages in
four days. At that rate,
how many days would
it take her to read a
300-page book?

h. Six pairs of socks cost
$4.50. What do 30 pairs
of socks cost?

3. These problems are more challenging.

a. Five collectible cars cost $35.50.
What would four cars cost?

b. Margie can weed five rows of strawberry
plants in 1 hour and 40 minutes. How long
would it take her to weed nine rows?

c. Elaine can run around the track four
times in an hour. Today, she only ran
around the track three times, and then
walked around it the fourth time. In all,
this took her 10 minutes longer than her
normal schedule. How many minutes did
it take her to walk around the track,
assuming that she ran at the same pace
as usual?

Multiplying Two-Digit Numbers in Parts

The picture illustrates the multiplication
18×27 using an area model.

The sides of the <u>whole</u> rectangle are 18
and 27. It is divided into four parts.
The areas of the partial rectangles are:

$10 \times 20 = 200$ (top left)
$10 \times 7 = 70$ (top right)
$8 \times 20 = 160$ (bottom left)
$8 \times 7 = 56$ (bottom right)

Of course, we add those to find the total area:

$200 + 70 + 160 + 56 = 486$ square units

	20	7
10	10 x 20	10 x 7
8	8 x 20	8 x 7

$$18 \times 27 = \quad 10 \times 20 + 10 \times 7$$
$$+ \ 8 \times 20 + 8 \times 7$$
$$= 200 + 70 + 160 + 56 = \underline{\textbf{486}}$$

1. Fill in the missing numbers. Write the area of the *whole* rectangle as a SUM of the areas of the
   smaller rectangles. Also find the total area.

a. $23 \times 31 =$ _____ × _____ + _____ × _____

$\quad$ + _____ × _____ + _____ × _____

$\quad =$ _____ + _____ + _____ + _____

$\quad =$ _____

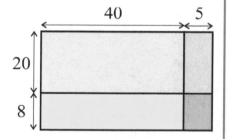

b. $28 \times 45 =$ _____ × _____ + _____ × _____

$\quad$ + _____ × _____ + _____ × _____

$\quad =$ _____ + _____ + _____ + _____

$\quad =$ _____

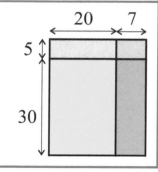

c. _____ × _____ = _____ × _____ + _____ × _____

$\quad$ + _____ × _____ + _____ × _____

$\quad =$ _____ + _____ + _____ + _____

$\quad =$ _____

2. It is your turn to draw. Draw a four-part rectangle to illustrate the multiplications, as it is in the previous problem. You don't have to draw to scale —a sketch is good enough.

a. $13 \times 27 =$

_____ × _____ + _____ × _____

+ _____ × _____ + _____ × _____

=

b. $36 \times 25 =$

_____ × _____ + _____ × _____

+ _____ × _____ + _____ × _____

=

c. $28 \times 49 =$

_____ × _____ + _____ × _____

+ _____ × _____ + _____ × _____

=

We can also use our "easy way" of multiplying with two 2-digit numbers. The calculation will have FOUR parts, just like the area model you just studied.

Let's multiply **56 × 28** in four parts: 6 × 8, 6 × 20, 50 × 8, and 50 × 20.

```
    2 8          2 8          2 8          2 8            2 8
  × 5 6        × 5 6        × 5 6        × 5 6          × 5 6
  ─────        ─────        ─────        ─────          ─────
    4 8          4 8          4 8          4 8            4 8
               1 2 0        1 2 0        1 2 0          1 2 0
                            4 0 0        4 0 0          4 0 0
                                       1 0 0 0        +1 0 0 0
                                                      ───────
                                                       1 5 6 8
```

First multiply 6 × 8.

Then 6 × 20.

Notice the "2" means 20, not just 2!

Next, 50 × 8.

Notice the "5" means 50.

Then, 50 × 20. Notice the "5" means 50 and the "2" means 20!

Lastly add.

3. It is your turn to practice. Multiply the numbers in four parts, and lastly add.

a.

```
        8 7
      × 1 5
```

$5 \times 7 \rightarrow$

$5 \times 80 \rightarrow$

$10 \times 7 \rightarrow$

$10 \times 80 \rightarrow$ +

b.

```
        2 4
      × 7 1
```

$1 \times 4 \rightarrow$

$1 \times 20 \rightarrow$

$70 \times 4 \rightarrow$

$70 \times 20 \rightarrow$ +

c.

```
        3 8
      × 9 2
```

$\_\_ \times 8 \rightarrow$

$\_\_ \times 30 \rightarrow$

$90 \times 8 \rightarrow$

$90 \times 30 \rightarrow$ +

d.

```
        5 2
      × 6 5
```

$\_\_ \times \_\_ \rightarrow$

$\_\_ \times \_\_ \rightarrow$

$60 \times 2 \rightarrow$

$60 \times 50 \rightarrow$ +

4. Multiply.

a.	**b.**	**c.**	**d.**
5 5 × 1 2	8 1 × 6 4	7 3 × 8 0	9 9 × 1 1
+	+	+	+
_____	_____	_____	_____

5. Multiply in four parts using the "easy way." Draw an area model to illustrate each multiplication.

a.   2 4
        × 1 7
        ‾‾‾‾‾

    +
    _____

b.   4 4
        × 3 9
        ‾‾‾‾‾

    +
    _____

133

6. Multiply in four parts using the "easy way." Draw an area model to illustrate each multiplication.

a.
$$
\begin{array}{r}
6\ 2 \\
\times\ 3\ 3 \\
\hline
\end{array}
$$

+ _____

b.
$$
\begin{array}{r}
4\ 7 \\
\times\ 5\ 3 \\
\hline
\end{array}
$$

+ _____

c.
$$
\begin{array}{r}
8\ 3 \\
\times\ 2\ 9 \\
\hline
\end{array}
$$

+ _____

Multiply by Whole Tens in Columns

$7 \times 58 = 406$. Now, based on that, what would 70×58 be? Can you guess?	$\begin{array}{r} 5 \\ 5\ 8 \\ \times\ \ 7 \\ \hline 4\ 0\ 6 \end{array}$

$116 \times 9 = 1{,}044$. Based on that, what would 116×90 be? Can you guess?	$\begin{array}{r} 1\ \ 5 \\ 1\ 1\ 6 \\ \times\ \ \ \ 9 \\ \hline 1\ 0\ 4\ 4 \end{array}$

Don't read more until you think about the questions above!

70×58 $= 10 \times 7 \times 58$ So, the result to 70×58 is ten times the result to 7×58. Since $7 \times 58 = 406$, then 70×58 is $4{,}060$. Just tag a zero!	116×90 $= 116 \times 9 \times 10$ So, the result to 116×90 is *ten* times the result to 116×9. Since $116 \times 9 = 1{,}044$, then 116×90 is $10{,}440$. Just tag a zero!

1. Use the above method to solve these problems.

a. $60 \times 87 = $ _____	**b.** $51 \times 40 = $ _____	**c.** $66 \times 30 = $ _____
(First multiply 6×87)	(First multiply $51 \times$ ____)	(First multiply ____ $\times$ ____)
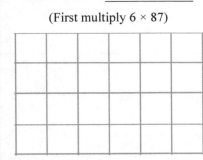	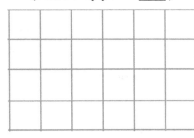	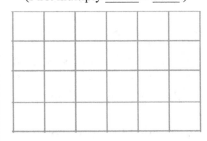

2. **a.** A crate of apples weighs 20 kg.
   How much do 65 crates weigh?

   b. One crate contains four layers of apples.
   There are 25 apples in each layer.
   How many apples are in a crate?

   c. A store owner sold 60 kg of apples to one customer.
   How many apples did the customer get?

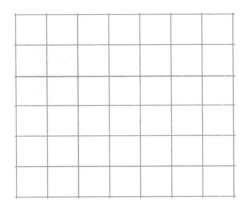

```
    1 3
  5 2 8
×     4
─────────
2 1 1 2 0 0
```

To multiply 5,280 × 40, you can first multiply 528 × 4 (without the ending zeros), and then write *two* **zeros after the answer**.

We get 5,280 × 40 = 211,200.

3. Multiply. First multiply without the ending zeros, then add them to the answer.

a. 800 × 46 = _____

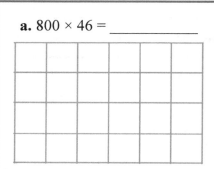

b. 850 × 30 = _____

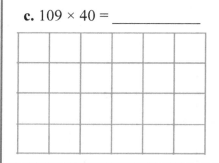

c. 109 × 40 = _____

d. 120 × 70 = _____

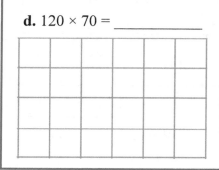

e. 400 × 335 = _____

f. 1,620 × 40 = _____

4. Mr. Hendrickson drives his bus about 250 km each day on his route. About how many kilometers does he drive during his 5-day work week?

   How much in the 4 weeks he works in a month?

5. *One* side of farmer Greg's square field measures 200 m. He jogged around the square seven times. What is the distance he jogged?

6. Calculate 65,000 − 50 × 430. Use a notebook.

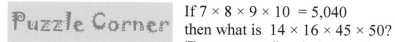

Puzzle Corner

If 7 × 8 × 9 × 10 = 5,040 then what is 14 × 16 × 45 × 50?
(Try not to actually calculate in columns! There is a quicker way.)

Multiplying in Parts: Another Way

(This lesson is optional)

You have learned to do 7 × 82 in parts: first multiply 7 × 80 and then 7 × 2. The same idea works when we have two 2-digit numbers.

Let's solve **25 × 34**. To find 25 times some number we can find 20 times the number and 5 times the number, and then add those two. So we break 25 × 34 into two parts: 20 × 34 and 5 × 34.

Example 1: 25 × 34			Example 2: 78 × 47		
Do 20 × 34. Don't forget the extra zero.	Then do 5 × 34.	Then add the parts.	Do 70 × 47. Remember the extra zero.	Then do 8 × 47.	Then add the parts.

Example 1:

```
      3 4          2
    × 2 0         3 4          6 8 0
    —————       ×   5        + 1 7 0
    6 8 0       —————        —————
                1 7 0          8 5 0
```

Example 2:

```
      4              5
    4 7            4 7          3 2 9 0
  × 7 0          ×   8        +   3 7 6
  —————          —————        —————
  3 2 9 0          3 7 6        3 6 6 6
```

1. Break the multiplications into two parts. You don't have to find the answer.

a. 28 × 16 = __20__ × 16 and __8__ × 16	**b. 48** × 73 = _____ × 73 and ____ × 73
c. 19 × 42 = _____ × 42 and ____ × 42	**d. 55** × 89 = _____ × 89 and ____ × 89

2. Find the final answers for the problems in (1).

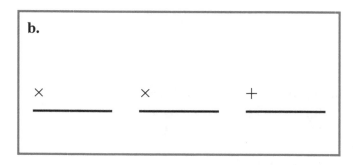

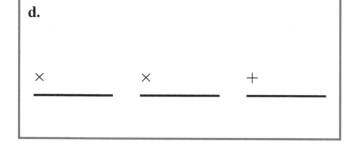

3. Break the multiplications into two parts. Then calculate to find the final answer.

a. <u>**46**</u> × 41 = ____ × ____ and ____ × ____

× _____   × _____   + _____

b. <u>**28**</u> × 39 = ____ × ____ and ____ × ____

× _____   × _____   + _____

c. 15 × 27 = ____ × ____ + ____ × ____

× _____   × _____   + _____

d. 93 × 16 = ____ × ____ + ____ × ____

× _____   × _____   + _____

Solve. Estimate before you calculate.

4. It costs Mary $27 per month for Internet service. How much does Mary pay per year for Internet?

Estimation:

5. Find the product 1 × 2 × 3 × 4 × 5 × 6.

6. A store sells 15-kg boxes of apples for $35 a box. If you buy 12 boxes, what is their total weight?

Estimation:

7. What is the total cost for 12 boxes of apples?

Estimation:

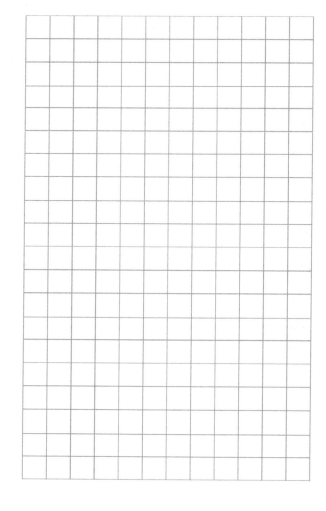

The Standard Multiplication Algorithm with a Two-Digit Multiplier

You have learned to calculate multiplications such as 67 × 53 in parts.
You did two multiplications and then added. It took three separate calculations.

In the traditional way of multiplying there are also three separate calculations, but all three calculations appear together. Study how we solve **67 × 53** below.

```
      2              1 2            1 2
    5 3            5 3            5 3
  × 6 7          × 6 7          × 6 7
  ─────          ─────          ─────
  3 7 1          3 7 1          3 7 1
               3 1 8 0        + 3 1 8 0
                              ─────────
                                3 5 5 1
```

First multiply **7 × 53**.
Pretend the 6 of
the 67 is not there.

Then multiply **60 × 53**, but write the result under the 371. Remember the zero. Pretend that the 7 of the 67 is not there. You can cross out the carry number from the previous calculation, so you won't get confused by it.

Lastly add.

Study these examples, too. <u>Note we need an extra zero</u> in the ones place on the second line!

5 × 34	**20 × 34**	Add.	**4 × 63**	**90 × 63**	Add.

```
    2
  3 4          3 4          3 4
× 2 5        × 2 5        × 2 5
─────        ─────        ─────
1 7 0        1 7 0        1 7 0
             6 8 0      + 6 8 0
                        ───────
                          8 5 0
```

```
  1
6 3          6 3          6 3
× 9 4        × 9 4        × 9 4
─────        ─────        ─────
2 5 2        2 5 2        2 5 2
             5 6 7 0    + 5 6 7 0
                        ─────────
                          5 9 2 2
```

1. Fill in the missing digits and complete the calculations.

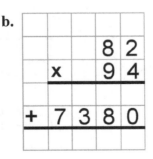

a.
```
      6 5
  ×   1 8
  ───────

+   6 5 0
  ───────
```

b.
```
      8 2
  ×   9 4
  ───────

+ 7 3 8 0
  ───────
```

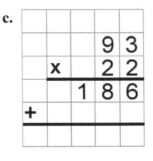

c.
```
      9 3
  ×   2 2
  ───────
    1 8 6
+
  ───────
```

d.
```
      7 0
  ×   5 3
  ───────
    2 1 0
+
  ───────
```

2. Multiply.

a.
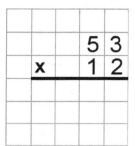

b.
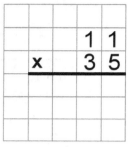

c.
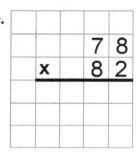

d.
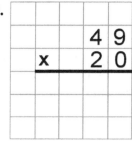

e.
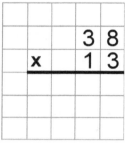

f.
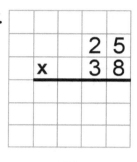

g.
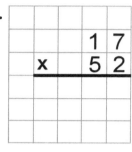

h.
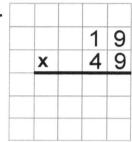

3. Multiply – but first, estimate the result. Compare your final answer to your estimated answer.
   If there is a big difference, you might have an error somewhere.

a. Estimate: _____ × _____

= _____

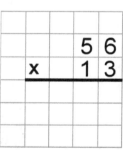

b. Estimate: _____ × _____

= _____

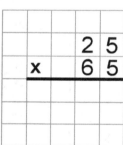

c. Estimate: _____ × _____

= _____

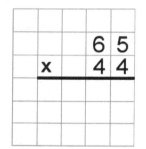

d. Estimate: _____ × _____

= _____

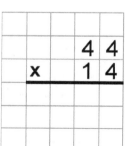

e. Estimate: _____ × _____

= _____

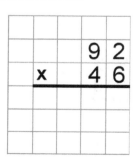

f. Estimate: _____ × _____

= _____

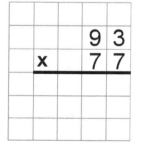

4. Multiply – but first, estimate the result.

a. Estimate: _____ × _____

= _____

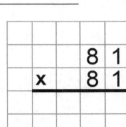

```
      8 1
  x   8 1
```

b. Estimate: _____ × _____

= _____

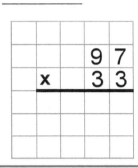

```
      9 7
  x   3 3
```

c. Estimate: _____ × _____

= _____

```
      2 8
  x   5 4
```

5. Solve the word problems. Write a number sentence for each one. Give more than just the final answer.

a. How many eggs is 15 dozen eggs?

_____

Estimate: _____

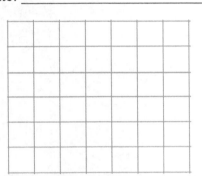

b. How many minutes are there in 21 hours?

_____

Estimate: _____

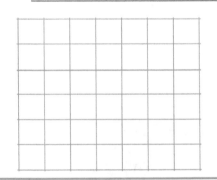

c. The 455 pupils in a school are going to a zoo by bus. One bus can seat 39 passengers. Are 11 buses enough to take them all?

_____

Estimate: _____

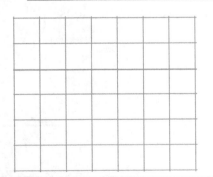

d. Each month, Brenda earns $21 for watering her neighbor's flowers. How much does she earn in a year?

_____

Estimate: _____

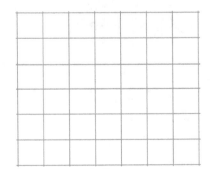

6. **a.** Is the answer to 53 × 61 he same as to 51 × 63?
   After all, it is just switching the ones digits.

   b. What about 42 × 71 and 41 × 72?
   If they are not the same, how much is
   the difference?

7. Find the change, if a teacher buys 15 shirts
   for $17 each and pays with $300.

8. One year has 52 weeks. Sally pays $98 weekly
   in rent. How much will she pay in a year?

9. Calculate in the correct order.

a. 60 × (10 + 20) × 2 = _____
30 × (40 − 40) × 2 = _____
b. 8 × (200 − 100) − 500 = _____
(800 − 200) × 20 + 100 = _____

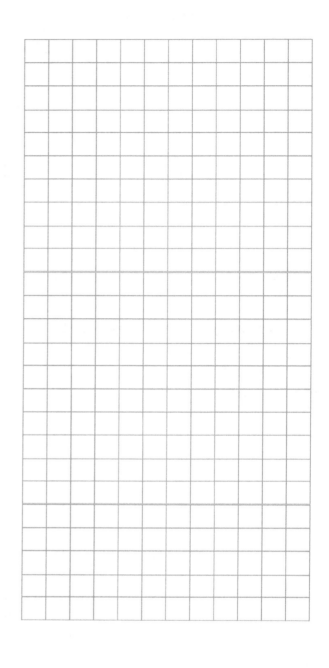

 Fill in the missing numbers in these multiplications:

```
  ☐ 0 ☐          6 ☐ 7          ☐ 3 ☐          8 ☐ 4
×     3        ×     ☐        ×     4        ×     5
───────        ───────        ───────        ───────
  3 1 5        4 0 0 2        9 ☐ 6          4 ☐ 7 ☐
```

Mixed Review Chapter 3

1. Solve mentally. (Order of Operations /Ch.1)

    a. $2{,}000 - (500 + 100) = $ _____

    b. $7{,}000 - (3{,}200 - 200) = $ _____

    c. $5{,}000 + (1{,}000 - 900 + 100) = $ _____

    d. $740 - (550 - 200 + 50) = $ _____

    e. $(900 - 200) - (300 + 200) = $ _____

    f. $1{,}000 + (5{,}000 - 500) + (4{,}000 - 500) = $ _____

2. Write the numbers and x in the bar model. Notice carefully what number is the total.
   Then write another matching subtraction that helps you solve x. (Bar Models in Addition and Subtraction/Ch.1)

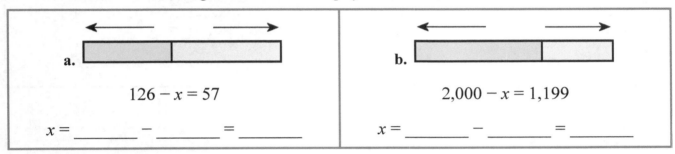

   a. $126 - x = 57$

   $x = $ _____ $-$ _____ $= $ _____

   b. $2{,}000 - x = 1{,}199$

   $x = $ _____ $-$ _____ $= $ _____

3. Round the numbers (as the dashed line indicates) to the underlined digit.
   (Rounding and Estimating Large Numbers/Ch.2)

a. 44<u>3</u>,920 ≈	**b.** 21<u>9</u>,506 ≈	**c.** 617,<u>0</u>74 ≈
d. 19<u>9</u>,734 ≈	**e.** <u>3</u>27,100 ≈	**f.** 8<u>1</u>,226 ≈

4. Multiply using the shortcut. (Multiplying by Whole Tens and Hundreds/Ch.3)

a. $76 \times 100 = $ _____ $40 \times 100 = $ _____	**b.** $10 \times 619 = $ _____ $10 \times 2{,}670 = $ _____	**c.** $98 \times 1{,}000 = $ _____ $1{,}000 \times 430 = $ _____

5. Use the shortcut "backwards" to solve the divisions. (Multiplying by Whole Tens and Hundreds/Ch.3)

a. $1{,}560 \div 10 = $ _____ $800 \div 10 = $ _____ $8{,}400 \div 100 = $ _____	**b.** $700 \div 10 = $ _____ $15{,}000 \div 100 = $ _____ $46{,}400 \div 100 = $ _____	**c.** $21{,}000 \div 1000 = $ _____ $999{,}000 \div 100 = $ _____ $1{,}000{,}000 \div 1000 = $ _____

6. Solve in the correct order. (Order of Operations Again/Ch.3)

a. $90 + 15 + 2 \times 7 =$ _____	**b.** $500 - 7 \times 70 - 10 =$ _____
$90 \times 10 + 120 - 40 =$ _____	$10 \times 7 \times 5 + 100 + 250 =$ _____

7. Compare, and write $<$, $>$, or $=$ in the boxes.

a. 100×26 ☐ 40×70 **b.** $5 + 195$ ☐ 40×5 **c.** 4×72 ☐ 300

8. Mason multiplied wrong. Find what mistake Mason made each time. Then correct his mistakes.
(Multiplying in Columns - the Standard Way/Ch.3)

```
    5                    6                     2
    4 8                  4 8                 2 3 9
 ×    7               ×    8               ×     3
 ───────              ───────              ───────
  2 8 6               3 2 4                 6 9 7
```

9. Solve.

a. Mick earned $345 for picking strawberries, and Jeanine earned three times as much. How much did they earn in total?

_____

_____

_____

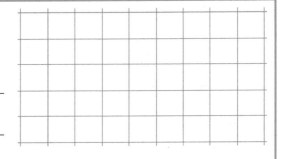

b. A grocery store pays out $145,600 in salaries and $12,390 in other expenses *each* month. Calculate its total expenses for June, July, and August.

Are the total expenses more than half a million dollars?

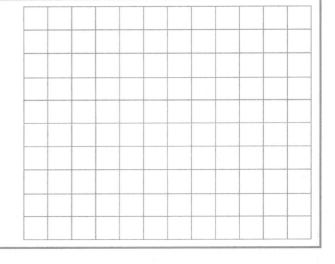

Review Chapter 3

1. Multiply.

a. 400 × 3 = _____	**b.** 70 × 60 = _____	**c.** 90 × 900 = _____
9 × 20 = _____	300 × 11 = _____	100 × 400 = _____

2. Find the missing factors. Think of how many zeros you need.

a. _____ × 50 = 4,000	**b.** 70 × _____ = 280	**c.** _____ × 40 = 12,000
_____ × 50 = 350	7 × _____ = 2,800	_____ × 800 = 64,000

3. Solve the equations.

a. 4 × 30 = $\underline{?}$ × 3	**b.** y × 500 = 250 × 4	**c.** 450 + 350 = △ × 20
$\underline{?}$ = _____	y = _____	△ = _____

4. Solve this problem using **estimation**.
   If you earn $515 weekly, in how many weeks
   will you have earned more than $4,000?

5. Multiply. Estimate the answer on the line.

a. 7 × 48	**b.** 6 × 813	**c.** 21 × 18	**d.** 4 × 5,903
≈ _____	≈ _____	≈ _____	≈ _____

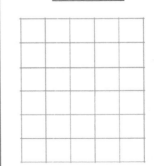
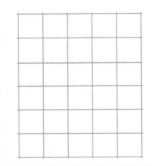

6. Fill in the table.

Roses	1	2	3	4	5	6	7	8
Price	$0.90							

7. Calculate in the right order.

$2 \times 98 - 8 \times 17$

8. Solve.

a. $(1{,}500 - 1{,}000) \times 4 = $ _____

b. $(76 + 34) \times 2 \times 0 = $ _____

c. $8 \times 2 \times (3 + 2) = $ _____

d. $200 \times (500 - 400) = $ _____

9. Draw a rectangle with several parts to illustrate the multiplications. You don't have to draw accurately — a sketch is good enough.

a. 8×24

= ___ × _____ + ___ × ___

= _____

b.
$$
\begin{array}{r}
3\,5 \\
\times\ 3\,9 \\
\hline
\end{array}
$$

+ _____

10. Solve. Write a number sentence for each one, not just the answer.

a. A store owner bought 50 boxes of shirts, with 20 shirts in each box, and each shirt costs $2. What was the total cost?

_____

_____

b. Dad bought 8 boxes of nails for $2.35 a box. What was his change from $20?

_____

_____

c. Charlene bought five ice cream cones for $1.50 each. Now she has $12.50 left. How much did she have originally?

_____

_____

d. A huge roll of wrapping paper costs $45 but it was discounted by $8. How much do five rolls cost?

_____

_____

11. Solve the problems. You can use the tables to help.

a. A dog can run three miles in 15 minutes. How far could it run in 10 minutes?

b. Seven cans of tuna weigh 420 g. How much would ten cans weigh?

147

Chapter 4: Time and Measuring
Introduction

The fourth chapter of *Math Mammoth Grade 4* includes lessons on time, temperature, length, weight, and volume. The focus is no longer on the actual act of measuring, but on conversions between the units and on word problems that involve conversions.

We start out studying clock and time, with a focus on elapsed time. In contrast to third grade, the time intervals can now include the change from AM to PM, and the given times do not follow five-minute increments. The lessons give several strategies for finding the elapsed time. Students also make schedules and solve a variety of word problems involving time.

Conversions between measurement units is a big focus point of the chapter. Students may have difficulties with this, and that is why this topic will also be studied in 5th grade. At this point, students should be able to easily convert a bigger unit into a smaller unit (such as converting 3 feet into 36 inches or 2 kg into 2,000 grams).

While the Common Core standards do not include them for fourth grade, I have also included some problems where we convert from a smaller unit to a bigger unit (such as 4,500 ml into 4 L 500 ml or 12 feet into 4 yards) because I feel most children are capable of doing these in fourth grade. If you feel your child has difficulty with converting from a smaller unit to a bigger one, feel free to omit those particular exercises. They are intermixed though, and not marked in any special way.

The chapter includes separate lessons for customary and metric units. Each lesson dealing with measuring units includes a table that lists the units we are studying and the conversion factors. For metric units, those tables always include all the units, even when they are not in common usage. For example, for metric units of volume, the chart looks like this:

liter	**L**	for larger amounts of liquid
deciliter	dl	(for medium amounts of liquid)
centiliter	cl	(for small amounts of liquid)
milliliter	**ml**	for small amounts of liquid

1 L = 1,000 ml   10, 10, 10, 10

The lesson deals only with milliliters and liters. However, the chart also shows the other two units (deciliters and centiliters) in order to help students become familiar with those basic units of the metric system:

1. The units always differ by a factor of ten;

2. The units are named consistently with the same prefixes (milli-, centi-, deci-, deka-, hecto-, and kilo-). These prefixes and their meanings are not yet studied in detail in fourth grade. You may, at your discretion, explain them to the student.

The Lessons in Chapter 4

Helpful Resources on the Internet

You can also access this list of links at **https://l.mathmammoth.com/gr4ch4**

DISCLAIMER: *We check these links a few times a year. However, we cannot guarantee that the links have not changed. Parental supervision is always recommended.*

ELAPSED TIME

Elapsed Time
Find how much time passes between two different given times (elapsed time or time intervals) in this customizable online exercise.
https://www.mathmammoth.com/practice/clocks

Elapsed Time
Click "New Time". Then click the buttons that advance the time on the clock, until the time matches the "End" time. Choose difficulty levels 1 and 2 for this grade level.
http://www.shodor.org/interactivate/activities/ElapsedTime/

Elapsed Time Worksheets
Generate printable worksheets for elapsed time. You can practice the elapsed time, finding the starting time, or finding the ending time.
https://www.mathnook.com/worksheets/elapsedtimeworksheets.php

Find the Start Time
Word problems about starting times with multiple-choice answers. Choose "full screen", then "Find the start time". Next, choose option 4 or 5.
https://mathsframe.co.uk/en/resources/resource/119/find_the_start_time

Time for Crime—Elapsed Time Mystery
A single mystery problem which can be solved by thinking of the elapsed time: who is the thief?
http://teacher.scholastic.com/maven/timefor/index.htm

ThatQuiz—Elapsed time
A ten-question quiz on Elapsed Time
https://www.thatquiz.org/tq-g/?-j4-l4-p0

Adding Time Word Problems
Read the time and then answer a word problem involving adding a given time.
https://mathsframe.co.uk/en/resources/resource/118/adding_time_word_problems

Converting Units of Time Quiz
Practice converting between various units of time with this multiple-choice quiz.
https://www.turtlediary.com/quiz/converting-units-of-time.html

Telling the Time
Practice reading the time on an analogue clock. Choose a level to practice, and then choose the option "24 hour clock".
https://mathsframe.co.uk/en/resources/resource/116/telling_the_time#

Interactivate: Elapsed Time
Practice calculating elapsed time with analog or digital clocks.
http://www.shodor.org/interactivate/activities/ElapsedTime/

Elapsed Time Quiz
A 10-question online quiz that practices elapsed time in hours and minutes.
https://www.thatquiz.org/tq-g/?-j4-l3-mpnv600-p0

TEMPERATURE

Thermo Quiz
Select the box that contains the temperature the thermometer is showing.
https://www.mathnook.com/math/thermometer-quiz.html

Reading a Thermometer in Degrees Celsius Quiz
An interactive multiple-choice quiz.
https://www.kidsmathtv.com/learn/reading-a-thermometer-in-degrees-celsius-quiz/

Sort the Temperatures Activity
Organize the scenarios in order from coldest to hottest.
https://www.mathnook.com/math/sort-the-temperatures.html

Hot Stuff
Practice estimating temperatures in Fahrenheit.
http://www.beaconlearningcenter.com/WebLessons/HotStuff/default.htm

Be a Scientist
Practice estimating temperatures in Celsius.
http://www.beaconlearningcenter.com/WebLessons/BeAScientist/default.htm

Temperature
Practice reading thermometers with different scales.
https://www.topmarks.co.uk/Flash.aspx?f=Temperaturev2

Temperature Quiz
Answer questions about reasonable temperatures in Fahrenheit and Celsius in this interactive multiple-choice quiz.
https://www.softschools.com/quizzes/math/temperature_measurement/quiz2112.html

Interactive World Map with Climate Graphs
Click on the dots on the map to see line graphs demonstrating the climates of various world cities.
https://www.digitalatlasproject.net/themes/climate-systems/climate-graphs

Temperature Line Graphs
This free downloadable activity includes interpretation of a line graph, followed by a challenge for students to draw their own line graph using temperature data from different cities, as well as writing their own questions for their completed graph.
https://www.tes.com/teaching-resource/temperature-line-graphs-6441279#

LENGTH

The Ruler Game
Click on the measurements on the ruler that correspond with the measurements that appear.
https://www.rulergame.net/

Reading a Ruler by Eighths
Practice reading a ruler by eighths with a matching exercise and a game of Concentration.
https://www.quia.com/jg/1364429.html

Measure It!
Practice measuring lines with either centimeters or inches. Multiple choice questions.
https://www.funbrain.com/games/measure-it

Sal's Sub Shop
Cut the subs to the given measurements—sometimes in metric units, sometimes in inches.
https://mrnussbaum.com/sal-s-sub-shop-online-game

Reading a Tape Measure Worksheets
Worksheet generator—choose to measure in inches, or inches and feet.
https://themathworksheetsite.com/read_tape.html

Funny Numbers - Length
Practice adding or subtracting amounts of feet and inches. Choose the option "Length" in the menu.
https://tangmath.com/funnynumbers

Convert to Smaller Units (in, ft, yd, & mi)
Practice converting between customary units of length in this interactive online exercise.
https://cutt.ly/Convert-customary-units-length

Convert to Smaller Units (mm, cm, m, & km)
Practice converting between metric units of length in this interactive online quiz.
https://cutt.ly/Convert-metric-units-length

Metric Units of Length Matching Game
Practice converting metric units of length while also uncovering a hidden picture.
https://www.mathmammoth.com/practice/measurement-units#tiles=24&level=2&opts=km-m,m-cm,m-mm,cm-mm

Quiz on metric units of length
Practice converting between metric units of length in this 10-question quiz.
https://www.thatquiz.org/tq-n/?-j147-l2-p0

WEIGHT

Funny Numbers - Weight
Practice adding or subtracting amounts of pounds and ounces. Choose the option "Weight" in the menu.
https://tangmath.com/funnynumbers

Reading Scales
Illustrate how to read a scales or a thermometer. Use the buttons to generate new scales and measurements.
https://www.teacherled.com/iresources/scales/mass/

https://www.teacherled.com/iresources/scales/temperature/

Ounces, Pounds, and Tons
Answer questions about customary units of weight in this jeopardy-style game.
https://www.quia.com/cb/426998.html

Convert to Smaller Units (g and kg)
Practice converting from kilograms to grams in this interactive exercise.
https://cutt.ly/Convert-Metric-Units-Weight

Estimate Mass (Grams and Kilograms)
Test your knowledge of metric units of weight with this short interactive quiz.
https://www.khanacademy.org/math/cc-fourth-grade-math/imp-measurement-and-data-2/imp-estimating-mass/e/estimating-mass?modal=1

VOLUME

Artie Ounces Soda Jerk
Practice standard units of volume with this fun soda jerk game. Fill the client orders as fast as you can!
https://mrnussbaum.com/artie-ounces-soda-jerk-online-game

Standard Liquid Volume Matching Game
Match standard liquid volumes with equivalent volumes.
https://www.quia.com/mc/126277.html

MathPup Rocket Tank
Help MathPup fly into space by filling his jetpack with the exact amount of fuel needed (practices customary units of volume).
https://www.mathnook.com/math2/mathpup-rocket-tank.html

Estimate Volume (Milliliters and Liters)
Test your knowledge of metric units of volume with this short interactive quiz.
https://www.khanacademy.org/math/cc-fourth-grade-math/imp-measurement-and-data-2/imp-estimating-volume/e/estimating-volume?modal=1

GENERAL

Customary Units of Measurement Matching Game
Practice converting customary measurement units while also uncovering a hidden picture.
https://cutt.ly/customary-units-matching-game

Measuring
Worksheets, fact sheets, and quizzes that practice various measuring concepts in both metric and imperial units.
https://www.bbc.co.uk/teach/skillswise/measuring/zkvqcqt

Conversion Quizzes - ThatQuiz.org
A customizable online quiz about conversions between measuring units. The options include both metric and customary systems and six different difficulty levels.
https://www.thatquiz.org/tq-n/science/metric-system/

Time Units

Pay close attention and <u>memorize</u> these relationships between time units, if you don't know them yet.	1 minute = 60 seconds 1 hour = 60 minutes 1 day = 24 hours	1 week = 7 days 1 year = 12 months 1 year = 365 days

1. Fill in.

a.

Days	Hours
1	24
2	48
3	72
4	96
5	120
6	144
7	168
8	192

b.

Minutes	Seconds
1	60
2	120
3	180
4	240
5	300
6	360
7	420
8	480

c.

Years	Months
1	12
2	24
3	36
4	48
5	60
6	72
7	84
8	96

2. Solve. Write a number sentence for each question, not just the answer.

a. Brian puts $120 into his savings each month. After saving for half a year, he bought a keyboard for $399. How much does he have left of his savings?

he has 120 × 6 - 726
= $321 in his
savings.

$$120 \times 6 = 720$$
$$720 - 399 = 321$$

b. How much money do you spend in one year if you spend $3 for a candy bar every day for a year?

he spent 365 × 3
= $1095.

$$365 \times 3 = 1095$$

153

3. One hour is 60 minutes. Convert these times into minutes.

a. 5 h = _300_ min	**b.** 4 h 6 min = _246_ min	**c.** 8 h 18 min = _498_ min
10 h = _600_ min	3 h 37 min = _217_ min	20 h 10 min = _1,210_ min
12 h = _720_ min	7 h 50 min = _470_ min	12 h 3 min = _723_ min

---

- Add the hours and minutes separately.

- If the sum of the minutes is more than 60, then each 60 minutes in the sum makes an hour.

Here, 125 minutes is 60 + 60 + 5 minutes, so we get two new hours from all of those minutes. The initial answer of 10 hours 125 minutes is changed into 12 hours 5 minutes.

```
      6 h    50 m
      2 h    30 m
  +   2 h    45 m
  ─────────────────
     10 h   (125 m)

  =  12 h     5 m
```

---

4. Add the hours and minutes. Remember to convert the sum of minutes into hours and minutes.

a.	**b.**	**c.**	**d.**
2 h 20 m 1 h 30 m + 4 h 55 m 7h 105min =8h 45min	1 h 22 m 3 h 53 m + 5 h 40 m 9h 115m =6h 55m	2 h 55 m 2 h 46 m + 1 h 51 m 5h 152 =7h 32m	3 h 48 m 7 h 12 m + 4 h 37 m 14h 97m =15h 37m

---

5. Solve the problems.

a. If you watch a program that lasts 35 minutes each day, how much time do you spend watching it in a week? Give your answer in minutes, and *also* as hours and minutes.

_245m, 4h5m_

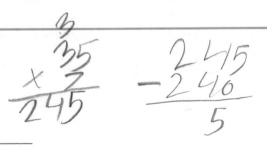

b. This is a chart of Bob's working hours at the bakery:

Monday	Tuesday	Wednesday	Thursday
2 h 30 min	3 h 50 min	1 h 10 min	3 h 25 min

How much time did he work in total during these 4 days?

_10h 55m_

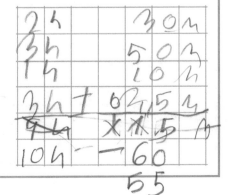

154

6. Solve.

a. Ashley kept track of how long she spent doing math homework:

Monday	Tuesday	Wednesday	Thursday	Sunday
45 min	35 min	1 h 10 min	1 h 5 min	40 min

How much time in total did she spend on math homework?

_____4h 15min_____

b. It takes about 40 minutes to drive from Raymond's home to town. His family is going to drive to town, spend about 3 hours shopping, and then come back home. What is the total amount of time they will be gone on their shopping trip?

4h 20m ✗

c. Joan finished the foot race in exactly two minutes, and Jean was 24 seconds faster. What was Jean's finishing time?

1 min 36 seconds

d. John stayed in bed for three whole days after his surgery. How many hours is that?

72h

e. You walk your dog about 25 minutes each day. About how long do you spend walking your dog in a week? Give your answer in hours and minutes.

2 h 55 min

How much time do you spend in four weeks (a month)?

700m 11hr 40min

f. Write a number sentence to find the number of seconds in one hour, and solve it.

60 × 60 = 3,600 s

155

Elapsed Time 1

<u>How many minutes is it from 1:47 to 2:10?</u>

Notice that the hour changes from 1 to 2. We need to calculate this carefully, but it is easy when you calculate it in two parts:

From 1:47 to 2:00 is 13 minutes. From 2:00 to 2:10 is 10 minutes. So the total is 23 minutes.

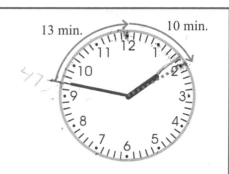

<u>How many minutes is it from 4:28 to 5:15?</u>

Again, the hour changes, so we figure it in two parts:
From 4:28 to 5:00 is 32 minutes. From 5 to 5:15 is 15 minutes. The total is: 32 + 15 = 47 minutes.

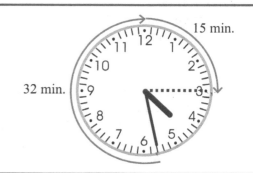

1. How many minutes is it from the time on the clock face until the given time?

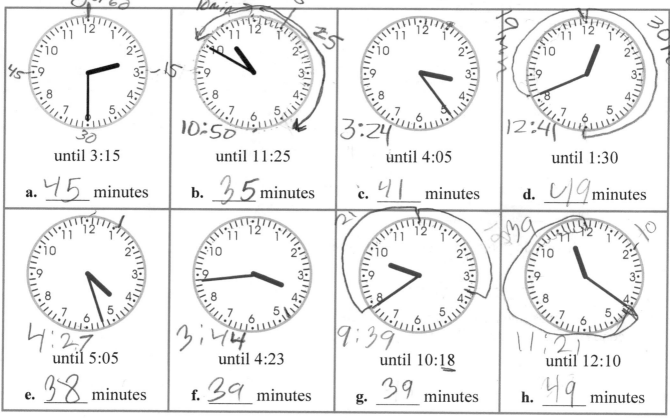

until 3:15	until 11:25	until 4:05	until 1:30
a. 45 minutes	b. 35 minutes	c. 41 minutes	d. 49 minutes

until 5:05	until 4:23	until 10:18	until 12:10
e. 38 minutes	f. 39 minutes	g. 39 minutes	h. 49 minutes

156

How much time passes from 5:38 to 8:38?

The minutes are the same (:38), so the minute hand has made some full rounds—full hours—and ended up back in the same place. So you need to only look at the *difference in the hours*: From 5 to 8 is 3 hours. Three hours have passed.

How much time passes from 11:30 to 4:30?

Once again, the minute hand has made several full rounds. From 11 to 4 is five hours.

You can also figure the passed time in parts:

(1) From 11:30 to 12:00 is half an hour.
(2) From 12:00 to 4:00 is four more hours.
(3) From 4:00 to 4:30 is another half an hour.

The total is five hours.

2. How much time passes during these intervals?

a. From 2:06 to 10:06 8 hr	**b.** From 8:25 to 12:25 4 hr	**c.** From 3:30 to 6:00 2 hr 30 min
d. From 7:30 AM to 1:30 PM 6 h	**e.** From 10:00 AM to 3:30 PM 5 hr 30 min	**f.** From 9:49 to 1:49 4 hr
g. From 5 AM to 5 PM 12 hr	**h.** From 11 PM to 12 noon 13 hr	**i.** From 6 AM to 4 PM 10 hr

3. Find the elapsed time in parts.

a. From 1:40 to 2:30

From 1:40 till 2:00	20 minutes
From 2 till 2:30	30 minutes
Total	50

b. From 7:30 AM to 3:10 PM

From 7:30 to 8:00	30 min
From 8:00 to 12:00	4 h
From 12:00 to 3:00	3 h
From 3:00 to 3:10	10 min
Total	7 h 40 min

12:15 swim (handwritten)

4. How much time passes? Figure it out in parts.

a. From 2:35 to 8:15	b. From 6:40 AM to 4:15 PM
2:35 to 3:00 — 25 min	6:40 to 7:00 — 20 min
3:00 to 8:00 — 5 hr	7:00 to 4:00 — 9 hr
8:00 to 8:15 — 15 min	4:00 + 4:15 — 15
5 hr 40 min	9 hr 35 min

5. An airplane took off at 3:35 PM and landed at 7:10 PM.
   How long was the flight?

   7:00 + 7:10 = 6   3:35 to 4:00 25   3 hr 35 min
   4:00 to 7:00 3 hr

6. Here is part of a television schedule. Answer the questions about the programs.

Channel 1	Channel 2	Channel 3
4:30 Nature film: Whales	4:30 Cooking Class	4:45 Afternoon Bits
5:30 Children's Story Time	5:05 Kids TV	5:15 Nature film: Bees and Honey
6:05 Early News	5:55 Quick News	6:20 Flash News
6:35 Shopping Spree Show	6:20 Nature Film: The Antarctic	6:40 The Silly Faces Show
7:05 The Week in Politics	7:25 Current Trends	7:20 Arnold's Kitchen

(handwritten: 30 beside Channel 1, 25 beside Channel 2, 26 beside Channel 3)

a. Each of the three channels has a nature film.
   List here how long each one of them lasts.

   1 hr   1 hr 5 min   1 hr 5 min

b. Which is the longer program, "Children's Story Time" or "Kids TV"?
   How many minutes longer?   *Kid's TV = 60 min*
   15   *childrens story time = 35*

c. Which channel has the *longest* news program?
   Channel 1
   Which one has the *shortest* news program?
   Channel 3

   What is the difference between the two programs in minutes?
   6

d. Megan changed channels like this:

   30 − 20 = 10   *50 − 35 = 15* (handwritten calculations)

   From 4:30 to 5:15 Channel 1
   From 5:15 to 6:20 Channel 3
   From 6:20 to 7:25 Channel 2

   Which programs did Megan watch (either totally or partially)?
   Nature film whals part, Nature film bees and honey all
   Nature film Antamica all

158

The 24-Hour Clock

As you know, the hour hand goes around the entire 12-hour clock face *two* times in one day. A day has 2 × 12 hours = 24 hours.

Instead of using a.m. and p.m. to indicate which "round" we are on, we can use the 24-hour clock. The hours are simply numbered from 0 to 23 (or sometimes from 1 to 24). The afternoon hours are those from 13 to 24.

The 24-hour time is commonly called the "military time" or astronomical time in the United States. In most countries of the world it is the dominant system used for bus, school, and TV schedules.

4 p.m. = 16:00

How do we change a time expressed in the 12-hour clock to the 24-hour clock?

- For a.m. times the numbers do not change.

- For p.m. times you add 12 to the hours.

The other way around, to change 24-hour clock times to 12-hour clock times, you subtract 12 hours from the afternoon times.

a.m. / p.m. system	24-hour clock
3:50 a.m.	3:50
noon 12:00	12:00
5:54 p.m.	17:54
10 p.m.	22:00
midnight	24:00

1:30 pm   13:30 pm

1. Change the times to the 24-hour clock times.

a. 5:40 a.m.	**b.** 8:00 p.m.	**c.** 6:15 p.m.	**d.** 11:04 a.m.
5 : 40	20 : 00	18 : 15	11 : 04

e. 12:30 p.m.	**f.** 4:35 p.m.	**g.** 11:55 p.m.	**h.** 7:05 p.m.
12 : 30	16 : 35	23 : 55	19 : 05

2. All the times below are in 24 hour clock times. Change them to the a.m. / p.m. times. Don't forget to add "a.m." and "p.m." after each of the times. (Hint: Two of the following times will not require changing.)

a. 15:00	**b.** 17:29	**c.** 4:23	**d.** 23:55
3 : 00 p.m.	5 : 29 pm	4 : 23 Am	11 : 55 pm

e. 14:30	**f.** 10:45	**g.** 16:00	**h.** 21:15
2 : 30 pm	10 : 45 Am	4 : 00 pm	9 : 15 pm

3. Study the bus schedule below. The times are given as (hours minutes) in the 24-hour clock time. Each column represents a bus that leaves from York Mills at a certain time, and arrives in Newmarket. There are a total of 12 different buses.

Stops:	Bus 1	Bus 2	Bus 3	Bus 4	Bus 5	Bus 6	Bus 7	Bus 8	Bus 9	Bus 10	Bus 11	Bus 12
York Mills	15 10	15 35	15 50	16 05	16 17	16 29	16 41	16 53	17 05	17 20	17 35	17 50
Yonge Street	15 17	15 42	15 57	16 12	16 24	16 36	16 48	17 00	17 12	17 27	17 42	17 57
Finch GO	15 28	15 53	16 08	16 23	16 35	16 47	16 59	17 11	17 23	17 38	17 53	18 08
Thornhill	15 42	16 07	16 22	16 37	16 49	17 01	17 13	17 25	17 37	17 52	18 07	18 22
Hillcrest Mall	15 50	16 15	16 30	16 45	16 57	17 09	17 21	17 33	17 45	18 00	18 15	18 30
Yonge & Bernard	16 02	16 27	16 42	16 57	17 09	17 21	17 33	17 45	17 57	18 12	18 27	18 42
Oak Ridges	16 09	16 34	16 49	17 04	17 16	17 28	17 40	17 52	18 04	18 19	18 34	18 49
Aurora	16 15	16 40	16 55	17 10	17 22	17 34	17 46	17 58	18 10	18 25	18 40	18 55
Newmarket	16 30	16 55	17 10	17 25	17 37	17 49	18 01	18 13	18 25	18 40	18 55	19 10

a. If you need to be at Newmarket by 5 p.m., which bus should you take from York Mills?

bus 2

b. If you need to be at Newmarket by 6 p.m., which bus should you take from York Mills?

bus 6

c. Each bus takes exactly the same amount of time to travel from York Mills to Newmarket. How much time is that?

1hr 20 min

d. Jack was going from Oak Ridges to Newmarket. He came to the bus stop at half past five and caught the first bus that came. When was he in Newmarket?

6:01 Pm

e. How many minutes does it take to travel in a bus from Thornhill to Aurora?

33 min

f. How many minutes does it take to travel from Yonge Street to Oak Ridges?

52 min

g. Mark lives in Thornhill and he goes to an art class in Newmarket that starts at 6:30 p.m. He has to walk for 15 minutes from the Newmarket bus stop to the art class. Which bus should he take from Thornhill?

bus 8

160

Elapsed Time 2

We can also find time differences by **subtracting** or **adding** the hours and minutes separately in their own columns.

Example 1. Find the elapsed time from 4:46 p.m. to 7:13 p.m. by subtracting. Notice, we cannot subtract 46 minutes from 13 minutes, so we need to **regroup 1 hour as 60 minutes**, adding 60 to the 13 minutes so that it becomes 73 minutes. Do NOT regroup 1 hour as 10 or 100 minutes!	$\begin{array}{rr} 6\text{ h} & 73\text{ m} \\ \cancel{7\text{ h}} & \cancel{13\text{ m}} \\ -\quad 4\text{ h} & 46\text{ m} \\ \hline 2\text{ h} & 27\text{ m} \end{array}$

Example 2. How much time passes between 9:42 p.m. and 2:45 a.m.?
 	
Here p.m. changes to a.m. It is safer to figure this out in parts:
  1. From 9:42 p.m. to 10 p.m. = 18 minutes
  2. From 10 p.m. to midnight = 2 hours
  3. From midnight to 2:45 a.m. = 2 h 45 min
 	
Lastly we ADD the three time periods (on the right).
 	
If you were to simply subtract the two times 9:42 and 2:45, you would get the time difference from 2:45 to 9:42, which is not correct.
	$\begin{array}{rr} & 18\text{ m} \\ 2\text{ h} & 0\text{ m} \\ +\quad 2\text{ h} & 45\text{ m} \\ \hline 4\text{ h} & 63\text{ m} \\[4pt] =\ 5\text{ h} & 3\text{ m} \end{array}$

1. How much time passes? Solve these in your head.

a. From 12:30 p.m. till 2 p.m. _____ h _____ min	**b.** From 4:35 p.m. till 6:15 p.m. _____ h _____ min	**c.** From 5:19 a.m. till noon _____ h _____ min
d. From 9:30 a.m. till 2:10 p.m. _____ h _____ min	**e.** From 7:58 p.m. till midnight _____ h _____ min	**f.** From 11:05 p.m. till 6:35 a.m. _____ h _____ min

2. How much time passes? Use subtraction.

a. From 4:53 p.m. till 8:26 p.m. $\begin{array}{r} 8\text{ h}\quad 26\text{ m} \\ -\ 4\text{ h}\quad 53\text{ m} \\ \hline \end{array}$	**b.** From 6:37 p.m. till 9:03 p.m.	**c.** From 2:45 a.m. till 8:14 a.m.

3. How much time passes? Use subtraction.

a. From 1:16 p.m. till 7:42 p.m.	**b.** From 4:45 p.m. till 11:12 p.m.	**c.** From 7:38 a.m. till 11:24 a.m.

4. How much time passes? Do it in two parts, since one time has a.m. and the other has p.m.

a. From 8:27 p.m. till 2:12 a.m.	**b.** From 9 a.m. till 5:16 p.m.
c. From 10:48 a.m. till 8:26 p.m.	**d.** From 2:15 a.m. till 1:08 p.m.
e. From 7:42 a.m. till 3:35 p.m.	**f.** From 6:56 a.m. till 1:18 p.m.

5. How much time passes? Now we use the 24-hour clock, so you can either use subtraction, or figure it out in parts.

a. From 8:27 till 13:45	**b.** From 6:30 till 17:10	**c.** From 9:45 till 23:25

6. Make a schedule for a doctor. He assigns 30 minutes for each patient, and after three patients, he takes a 20-minute break. Use the 24-hour clock.

	Time
Patient 1	8:00 - 8:30
Patient 2	
Patient 3	
break	
Patient 4	
Patient 5	
Patient 6	
break	

	Time
Patient 7	
Patient 8	
Patient 9	
break	
Patient 10	
Patient 11	
Patient 12	

7. Make a class schedule. Each class is 50 minutes with 5 minutes between them. The lunch break is 40 minutes.

Class	Time
Social Studies	8:00 -
Math	
Science	
English	

Class	Time
Lunch	
History	
P.E.	

8. (Optional) Make a schedule for yourself.

Elapsed Time 3

When does it end? Typically, we *add* the starting time and the elapsed time to find the time when something ends.

Example 1. A meeting starts at 2:30 p.m. and lasts for 1 hour 15 minutes. When will it end?

Simply add the hours to the hours and minutes to the minutes:

2 hours + 1 hour = 3 hours and 30 min + 15 min = 45 min. The meeting ends at 3:45 p.m.

Example 2. Jake started playing at 3:35 p.m. and played for 45 minutes. When did he stop?

We can add as we did above: 35 min + 45 min = 80 min to get a total time of 3 hours 80 minutes, but 80 minutes is more than one hour! We need to think of the 80 minutes as 60 + 20, because 60 minutes makes one hour. The final answer is 4 hours and 20 minutes, or 4:20 p.m.

Example 3. If it started raining at 10:53 and it rained for 4 hours and 40 minutes, when did the rain end?

We can add the starting time and the time that has elapsed (on the right). Note that the sum of the minutes is more than 60, so we convert the 93 minutes to 1 hour and 33 minutes. The final answer is 15:33 or 3:33 p.m.

$$
\begin{array}{r}
10\ \text{h}\ \ 53\ \text{m} \\
+\ \ 4\ \text{h}\ \ 40\ \text{m} \\
\hline
14\ \text{h}\ \ 93\ \text{m} \\
=\ 15\ \ \text{h}\ \ 33\ \text{m}
\end{array}
$$

1. When will it end?

   a. Guests will come at 3:40 p.m. and stay for two hours and 30 minutes.

   b. Mom will start cooking pizza at 13:45, and it will take her one hour and 40 minutes.

   c. The pool will open at 8 a.m. and be open for ten-and-a-half hours. When will it close?

   d. Jen's exam will take two-and-a-half hours, and start at 8:45 am.

   e. The airplane will take off at 18:08 and fly for three hours and 55 minutes.

   f. The food will be put into the oven at 5:47 p.m. for 35 minutes.

   g. Factory workers work in three shifts. How long is each shift?

   How many minutes do each two shifts overlap?

Shift 1	6:00 a.m. - 2:30 p.m.
Shift 2	2:00 p.m. - 10:00 p.m.
Shift 3	9:30 p.m. - 6:30 a.m.

When did it start?

We can subtract, think backwards, or use other strategies to find the starting time.

Example 4. An airplane landed at 4:30 p.m. The flight took 3 hours and 40 minutes. When did the plane take off?

Think backwards from the ending time. Start at 4:30 and imagine the minute hand traveling backwards 3 full rounds, and then 40 minutes. Where do you end up?

Alternatively, subtract in columns. You will again need to regroup one hour as 60 minutes. The answer of 50 minutes means the clock time was <u>12:50 p.m.</u>

$$
\begin{array}{r}
3h \quad 90\,m \\
\cancel{4\,h} \quad \cancel{30\,m} \\
-\; 3\,h \quad 40\,m \\
\hline
50\,m
\end{array}
$$

Example 5. A 55-minute class ended at 21:10. When did it start?

If it had lasted for one hour, it would have started at 20:10. It was 5 minutes shorter than that, so it started 5 minutes later, or at <u>20:15</u>.

2. Find the starting time.

    a. From _____ : _____ p.m. till 2:00 p.m. is 40 minutes.

    b. From _____ : _____ p.m. till 8:12 p.m. is 30 minutes.

    c. From _____ : _____ a.m. till 4:15 a.m. is 1 hour 30 minutes.

    d. From _____ : _____ p.m. till 7:34 p.m. is 4 hours 10 minutes.

    e. From _____ : _____ a.m. till 5:00 p.m. is 6 hours 20 minutes.

    f. From _____ : _____ p.m. till 4:30 p.m. is 2 hours 40 minutes.

3. Find the ending or starting time. Imagine the minute hand turning, or use your practice clock.

a. 6:15 → _____ 40 minutes	**b.** 2:03 → _____ 25 minutes	**c.** 11:30 → _____ 35 minutes
d. _____ → 5:50 35 minutes	**e.** _____ → 7:00 45 minutes	**f.** _____ → 12:10 20 minutes

4. Solve.

a. The Johnson family arrived in the city at 10:30 after riding in the car for 3 hours and 15 minutes. When did they leave home?

b. When should the Johnson family leave the city to make it back home by 20:00 (assuming the driving time back home is the same)?

c. Shannon kept a record of how long it took him to run the track through the woods. Complete the chart with the amount of time he spent running each day.

	Mo	Wd	Th	Fr	Sa
Start: End:	17:15 18:20	17:03 18:05	17:05 18:12	17:45 18:39	17:12 18:15
Running time:					

d. Find the total amount of time that Shannon spent running during the week.

e. Gordon works from 8:30 until 17:15 each day. He has a 30-minute lunch break and two 15-minute "coffee" breaks. How many hours and minutes does he actually work?

f. The air conditioner is kept running from 7:30 a.m. until 9 p.m. How many hours does the air conditioner run in a *week*?

g. An airplane is scheduled to take off at 3:40 p.m. and land at 5:10 p.m. The flight is delayed so that it leaves at 3:55 p.m. instead. When will it land?

Measuring Temperature: Celsius

Temperature tells us how hot or cold something is. Temperature is measured in degrees Celsius in many parts of our world. We use a little elevated circle ° to mean degrees. So, 24°C is "24 degrees Celsius".

The Celsius scale

The Celsius scale gets its name from the Swedish astronomer Anders Celsius (1701 – 1744). He developed the scale two years before his death. He used 0 for the boiling point of water and 100 for the freezing point of water. These two were reversed in 1745, so the two defining points for the Celsius scale became:

The freezing point of water	**0°C**
The boiling point of water	**100°C**

(under normal conditions)

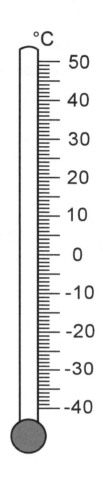

1. Mark these temperatures or temperature ranges on the side of the thermometer at the right.

Normal body temperature	37°C
Hot summer weather	25...35°C
Nice inside temperature	19...23°C
Below freezing (icy and snowy)	-40...0°C (negative)

2. Write the temperatures.

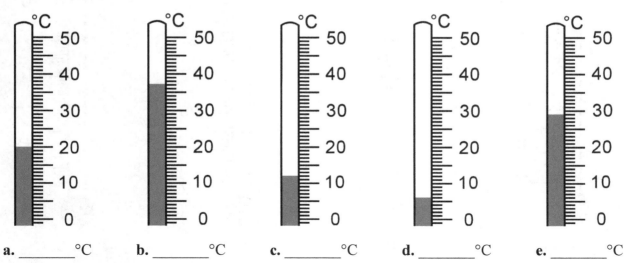

a. _____ °C   b. _____ °C   c. _____ °C   d. _____ °C   e. _____ °C

3. If you have a thermometer that measures in Celsius degrees, use it to measure the temperature:

    a. outside _____   **b.** inside _____   **c.** in the fridge _____

    You need to leave the thermometer in each place for about 10-15 minutes before reading it.

4. Check the weather forecast from the Internet: **https://www.bbc.com/weather/**

    Navigate to any area of the world you wish to. The temperatures are shown in
    Celsius degrees. Can you tell from the temperatures if it is cold, hot, warm, or cool?

5. In the box on the right, match
the temperatures with the
descriptions.

a fall day	5°C
a summer day	39°C
a fever	22°C
hot soup	55°C
boiling oil	-12°C
It is snowing!	200°C
inside a fridge	12°C
inside a house	21°C

6. Draw the liquid in the thermometers. Write the right description underneath:
    water freezing, a spring day, inside, a hot day

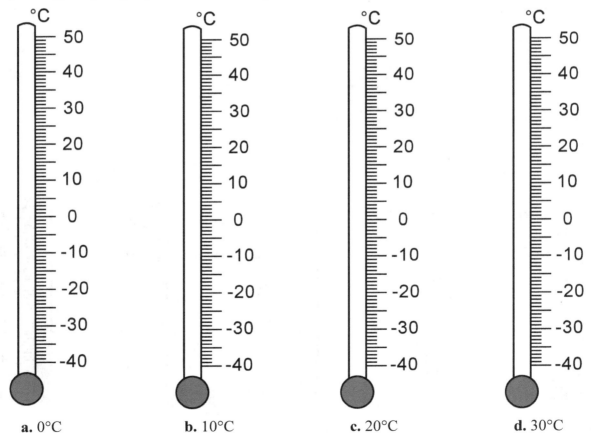

    a. 0°C   **b.** 10°C   **c.** 20°C   **d.** 30°C

Remember: **zero degrees Celsius is the freezing point of water**. Below that temperature, water turns to ice, and rain falls as snow.

When the temperature drops below 0 degrees, we use **negative numbers**. The temperature just 1 degree below zero is "minus one degree Celsius" or -1°C.

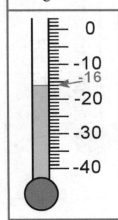

When reading negative numbers on a thermometer, you might call it "reading it backwards". The line just under 0 degrees matches -1°C.

The line below that is -2°C, and so on.

The thermometer on the right shows -4°C.

The thermometer on the left shows -16°C.

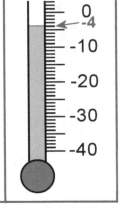

7. Read each thermometer and write the negative temperature it shows.

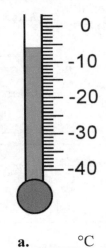 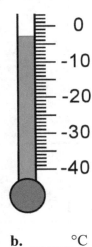 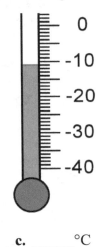 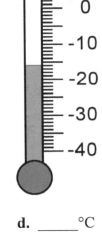 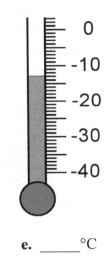

a. _____°C   **b.** _____°C   **c.** _____°C   **d.** _____°C   **e.** _____°C

8. Color the thermometers to show the given temperatures on the thermometers.

a. -5°C   **b.** -8°C   **c.** -12°C   **d.** -19°C   **e.** -23°C

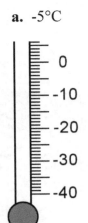 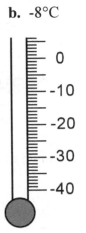 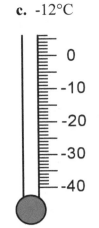 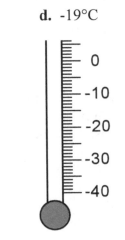 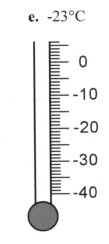

9. First write the temperature the thermometer shows. Then the temperature rises or falls. Color in the empty thermometer to show the new temperature.

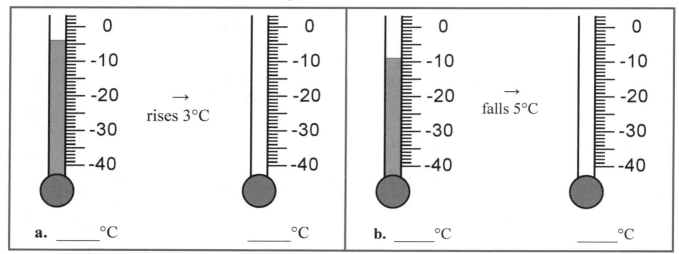

a. _____ °C   rises 3°C   _____ °C

b. _____ °C   falls 5°C   _____ °C

10. *Challenge.* The temperature rises or falls. Write the new temperature.

Now	temperature rises 1°C	After	Now	temperature falls 1°C	After	Now	temperature rises 3°C	After
a. -9°C		_____	b. -9°C		_____	c. -1°C		_____

Now	temperature rises 3°C	After	Now	temperature falls 5°C	After	Now	temperature falls 4°C	After
d. -13°C		_____	e. -7°C		_____	f. 2°C		_____

Now	temperature rises 5°C	After	Now	temperature falls 5°C	After	Now	temperature falls 3°C	After
g. -5°C		_____	h. 2°C		_____	i. -13°C		_____

11. The temperature inside a fridge is 5°C. The temperature inside the freezer is 20 degrees lower, and the temperature inside the room is 20 degrees higher than in the fridge.

   a. What is the temperature inside the freezer?

   b. What is the difference between the room temperature and that of the freezer?

Tuesday was a weird day. In the morning, the temperature was _____°C. Then, it fell 7°C and it started snowing. At noon, the temperature rose 8°C and the snow started melting!

Puzzle Corner

Lastly, late in the evening, the temperature dropped 3°C and it was down to 0°C. What was the temperature in the morning?

Measuring Temperature: Fahrenheit

Daniel Gabriel Fahrenheit was a German physicist who designed a scale for measuring temperature. This scale bears his name. The Fahrenheit scale is in common every-day usage in the United States. Other countries use the Celsius scale.

Temperature is measured in degrees. We use the ° symbol to mean a "degree". So 56°F is "56 degrees Fahrenheit."

Under normal conditions, when water freezes and becomes ice, its temperature is 32°F. And water boils at the temperature 212°F. These two temperatures are the two defining points for the Fahrenheit scale.

The Fahrenheit scale does have a zero, and below it we use negative numbers, as you do in centigrade.

The table lists some benchmark temperatures for the Fahrenheit scale:

Water boils at	212°F
Normal body temperature	98.6°F
Comfortable inside temperature	70-78°F
Water freezes at	32°F

Memorize this fact: **Water freezes at 32°F.**

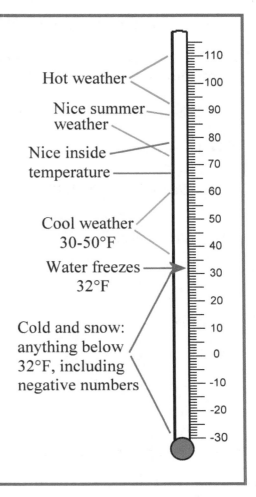

1. Write the temperatures that the thermometers show. Then match each temperature to one of the descriptions below:

Hot desert   Chilly day   Very warm day   Inside   Nice weather

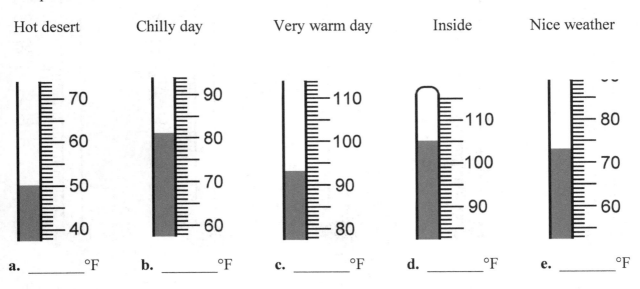

a. _____°F   b. _____°F   c. _____°F   d. _____°F   e. _____°F

2. If you have a thermometer that uses the Fahrenheit scale, use it to measure the temperature:

   a. outside _____   **b.** inside _____   **c.** in the fridge _____.

   You need to leave the thermometer in each place for about 10-15 minutes before reading it.

3. Check the weather forecast for some US city or state in a newspaper, on the TV, or Internet. Then discuss it with your teacher:

   • What temperature is forecast for your area?

   • For neighboring areas?

   • Is the weather hot, warm, cool, or cold?

4. Describe a situation to fit these temperatures.

   a. 33°F

   b. −12°F

   c. 102°F

5. Color each picture to show the given temperatures. Notice the scale: it is not in increments of one.

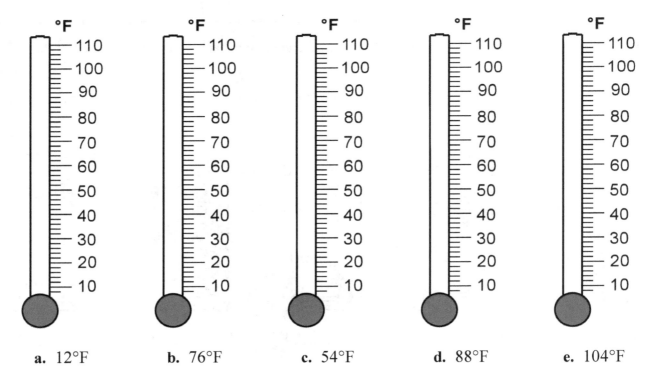

   a. 12°F   **b.** 76°F   **c.** 54°F   **d.** 88°F   **e.** 104°F

Temperature Line Graphs

1. Read the chart and fill in the table.

Month	Jan	Feb	Mar	Apr	May	Jun	Jul	Aug	Sep	Oct	Nov	Dec
Max Temperature												

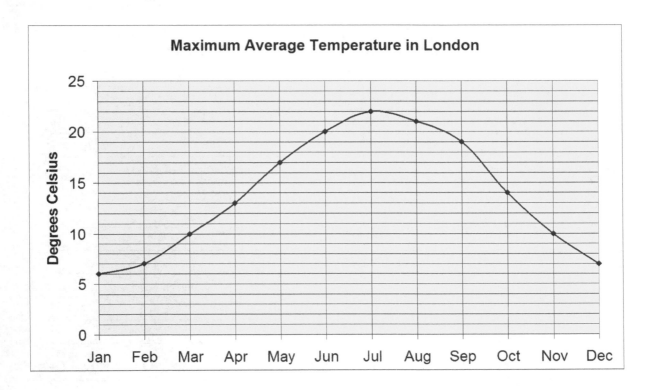

a. What is the hottest month?

b. What is the coldest month?

c. Find two months that have the same maximum average temperature.

d. What is the difference between the maximum temperature of May and that of June?

e. What is the difference between the maximum temperatures of June and July?

f. What is the difference between the maximum temperature of the coldest month and that of the hottest month?

2. Draw a line graph with the data.

Month	Minimum Temperature
Jan	-10
Feb	-9
Mar	-8
Apr	-2
May	-1
Jun	5

Month	Minimum Temperature
Jul	7
Aug	6
Sep	3
Oct	-4
Nov	-5
Dec	-7

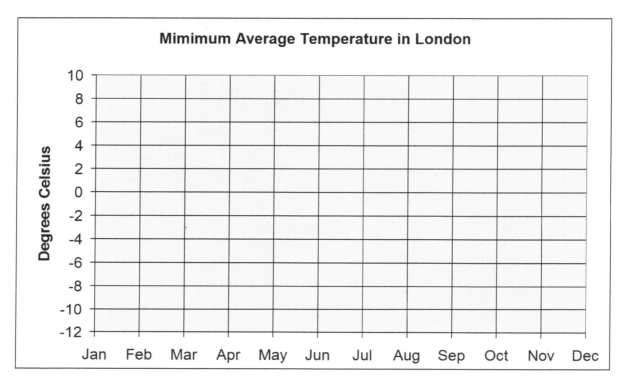

a. Which month is colder, January or March?

b. What is the difference between the minimum temperature of May and that of June?

c. What is the difference between the minimum temperatures of October and November?

d. How many degrees does the minimum temperature change from January to June?

Measuring Length

Remember? This ruler measures in inches. The three lines between each two numbers on the ruler divide each inch into *four* parts, which are **fourth parts of an inch**.

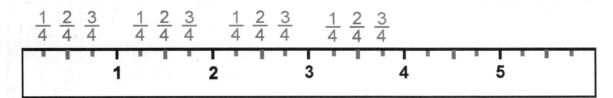

The 2/4 mark is also the 1/2 mark. (We normally use 1/2 instead of 2/4.)

This ruler measures in centimeters. The numbers signify whole centimeters. All the little lines between those are for millimeters.

There are 10 millimeters in each centimeter.

10 mm = 1 cm

The distance between these two is 1 mm.

1. Measure the lines to the nearest fourth of an inch.
   Also measure them in centimeters and millimeters.

a. _____ in. or _____ cm _____ mm

b. _____ in. or _____ cm _____ mm

c. _____ in. or _____ cm _____ mm

d. _____ in. or _____ cm _____ mm

e. _____ in. or _____ cm _____ mm

In the ruler below, each inch is divided into *eight* parts, which are **eighth parts of an inch**. The lines marking 1/4 inches are a little longer than the other lines, and the lines for half inches are a little longer yet.

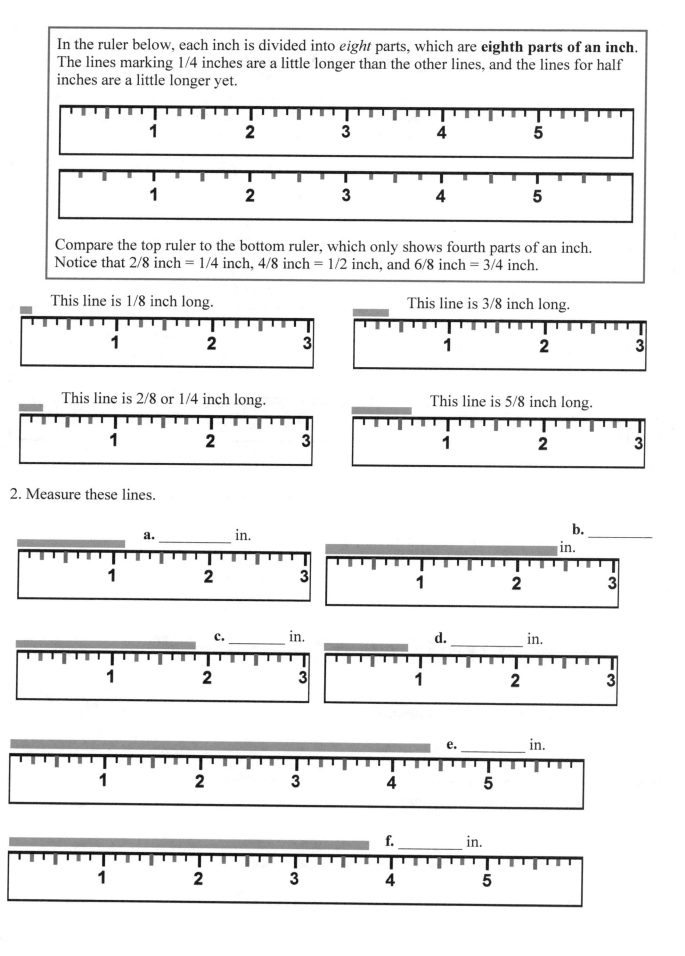

Compare the top ruler to the bottom ruler, which only shows fourth parts of an inch. Notice that 2/8 inch = 1/4 inch, 4/8 inch = 1/2 inch, and 6/8 inch = 3/4 inch.

This line is 1/8 inch long.

This line is 3/8 inch long.

This line is 2/8 or 1/4 inch long.

This line is 5/8 inch long.

2. Measure these lines.

a. _____ in.

b. _____ in.

c. _____ in.

d. _____ in.

e. _____ in.

f. _____ in.

3. Draw lines using a ruler.

    a. 3 1/8 inches

    b. 4 1/4 inches

    c. 5 7/8 inches

    d. 9 5/8 inches (turn your paper or book sideways)

    e. 7 1/2 inches

4. Draw lines using a ruler.

    a. 5 cm 3 mm

    b. 12 cm 1 mm

    c. 4 cm 4 mm

    d. 25 cm 7 mm (turn your paper or book sideways)

    e. 19 cm 9 mm

5. Measure the length of small items (pencils, pens, pins, erasers, books) using a ruler that has marks for eighth parts of an inch. Measuring tapes used for sewing can work, also. Or, you can cut out the ruler from the bottom of this page. (If you printed this page at a scale other than 100%, it will not be accurate.)

Item	Length/width

More Measuring in Inches and Centimeters

1. Spread one of your hands wide open and let someone measure the distance from the tip of your thumb to the tip of your little finger. This distance is your **span**. (The official span is 9 inches.)

   My *span* is _____ inches.

   Now use your span to measure the height of a table: The table is about _____ spans tall.

   Use that result to estimate the height of the table *in inches*. The table is about _____ in tall.

   Lastly check your estimate with a measuring tape: The table is _____ in tall.

   You can repeat this for other objects if you wish.

2. Find five small things. Before you measure them, *estimate* (guess) how long (or wide) each item is. Then, measure the items both in inches and centimeters.

Item	Guess (in)	Reality (in)	Guess (cm)	Reality (cm)

3. **a.** Measure all the sides of this figure to the nearest eighth of an inch. Write the measurements next to the sides of the figure.

   b. Measure its sides also in centimeters and millimeters.

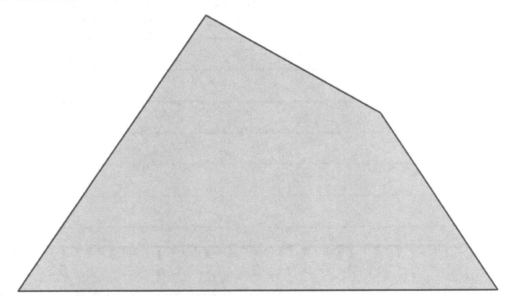

4. Use rulers and measuring tapes to find out which is a longer distance.

    a. 3 cm or 1 inch   **b.** 2 inches or 7 cm   **c.** 15 cm or 6 inches

5. *Challenge.* The perimeter of a rectangle is 8 cm. Its one side measures 2 cm 6 mm. How long is the other side?

6. Margaret measured the wing span of the butterflies in her butterfly collection and recorded the results in the line plot below.

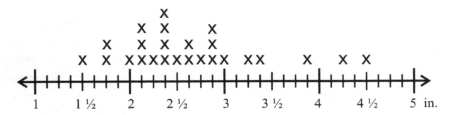

    a. How many butterflies have a wingspan from 2 to 2 1/2 inches?

    b. How many butterflies have a wingspan from 1 1/2 to 2 inches?

    c. How long is the wingspan of the largest butterfly?

    d. How long is the wingspan of the smallest butterfly?

    e. What is the difference in the wingspan of the largest and the smallest butterfly?

7. Find many small things you can measure to the nearest eighth of an inch, and make a line plot. For example, you could measure a bunch of pencils, many toy cars, the length of the middle finger of many people, or the length of many oak leaves (or leaves of some other tree).

Feet, Yards, and Miles

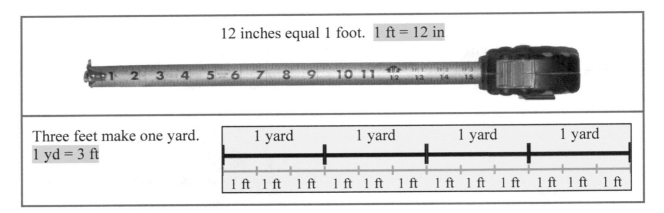

12 inches equal 1 foot. 1 ft = 12 in

Three feet make one yard.
1 yd = 3 ft

1. Use a tape measure to measure lengths of some objects and distances in feet and inches.

Item	How long
	_____ ft _____ in

2. Draw a long line at least 20 ft long (outside, if necessary) and make marks on it for 1 ft, 2 ft, 3 ft, and so on. Then walk along your line. First, try to take 1-foot steps. Then, try to take 2-foot steps. Then, try to take 1-yard steps.

   Which kind of steps were the most comfortable and easiest for you to take?

3. First, practice taking 2-foot steps on the line you drew. Then measure some distances by taking 2-foot steps. For example, measure the width of a street or the length of a room. Lastly figure out the distances in feet.

Distance	in steps	in feet

4. One foot is 12 inches. Fill in.

a.

Feet	Inches
1	
2	
3	
4	
5	

b.

Feet	Inches
6	
7	
8	
9	
10	

c.

Feet	Inches
11	
12	
13	
14	
15	

5. One foot is 12 inches. Convert between feet and inches.

a. 6 ft = _____ in 11 ft = _____ in	**b.** 2 ft 5 in = _____ in 7 ft 8 in = _____ in	**c.** 13 ft 7 in = _____ in 11 ft 11 in = _____ in
d. 36 in = _____ ft 50 in = _____ ft _____ in	**e.** 27 in = _____ ft _____ in 100 in = _____ ft _____ in	**f.** 64 in = _____ ft _____ in 85 in = _____ ft _____ in

6. Solve.

a. Sally is 4 ft 6 in tall, and Jerry is 5 ft 2 in tall. How many inches taller is Jerry than Sally?

b. Mia was 4 ft 10 in tall. Next year she grew three inches.
How tall is she now?

c. The world's *tallest* man is Sultan Kösen from Turkey. He measures 8 feet 3 inches.
The world's *shortest* man is Chandra Bahadur Dangi from Nepal. He is 1 foot 9 inches.

Figure out the difference in their heights!

d. *A challenge.* The long sides of a rectangle are 5 ft 6 in, and its perimeter 16 ft 10 in. How long are the shorter sides?

5 ft 6 in

5 ft 6 in

7. One yard is three feet. Fill in the tables.

Yards	Feet
1	
2	
3	

a.

Yards	Feet
4	
5	
6	

b.

Yards	Feet
7	
8	
9	

c.

8. One yard is 3 feet. Convert between yards and feet.

a. 6 yd = _____ ft 13 yd = _____ ft	**b.** 2 yd 2 ft = _____ ft 5 yd 1 ft = _____ ft	**c.** 24 ft = _____ yd 42 ft = _____ yd
d. 13 ft = _____ yd _____ ft 17 ft = _____ yd _____ ft	**e.** 22 ft = _____ yd _____ ft 29 ft = _____ yd _____ ft	**f.** 32 ft = _____ yd _____ ft 40 ft = _____ yd _____ ft

9. Jessie ran 400 yards and Andrew ran 1,000 feet. Who ran a longer distance?

How much longer?

10. This is a soccer field. Calculate the distance marked with (?).

   a. in yards

   b. in feet

11. Olivia bought 6 yards of material. She cut off
    two pieces that were 2 feet long each.
    Now how much material does she have left?

12. Olivia also cut a 1-yard piece of different material into two pieces.
    One piece was 1 ft 4 in long. How long is the remaining piece?

You can add feet to feet and inches to inches. Just remember that if you get more than 12 inches, each 12 inches makes a new foot.

Example 1.	Example 2.
Example 1. 2 ft 7 in + 1 ft 8 in = 3 ft 15 in = 4 ft 3 in Now, 15 inches is more than one foot—it is 1 foot 3 inches. So, we need to add one more foot to the 3 feet. The original answer 3 ft 15 in becomes 4 ft 3 in.	**Example 2.** When you add feet and inches in columns, again, check if the sum of the inches is 12 or more and makes an entire foot or feet. 3 ft 8 in + 6 ft 11 in ――――――― 9 ft 19 in = 10 ft 7 in

13. Solve.

a. The long sides of a rectangle are 6 ft 4 in, and the short sides are 2 ft 10 in. Mark the measurements around the rectangle.

Perimeter = _____ ft _____ in

b. Each side is 8 in.

Perimeter = _____ ft _____ in

c. Each side is 1 ft 8 in.

Perimeter = _____ ft _____ in

d. You have three pieces of furniture: a table, 5 ft 6 in long, a bed, 8 ft 3 in long, and a dresser, 3 ft 8 in long. Can they all fit along a wall that is 18 ft long?

e. A box is 2 ft 8 in tall. How tall is a stack of three of them?

A **mile** is used to measure long distances. **One mile is 5,280 feet**.

Mile originates from the Roman measure "mille passus," which means "thousand paces," where a pace is a double-step. The Roman mile was exactly 5,000 *Roman* feet.
Read in the links below how the 5,000-foot mile became a 5,280-foot mile around year 1300:

https://www.sizes.com/units/mile.htm and https://en.wikipedia.org/wiki/Furlong

14. Solve.

a. How many feet is four miles?

_____

_____

b. Convert 5 mi 2,350 ft into feet.

_____

_____

c. Which is a longer distance, 2 mi 800 ft or 13,000 ft? Use estimation (1 mile is *about* _____ ft).

_____

d. An airplane flies at the height of 21,000 feet.
About how many miles is that? _____

e. About how many miles tall is Mt. Everest (elevation 29,029 ft)? _____

f. Andrew can walk 300 feet in one minute. How many feet can he walk in 50 minutes?

_____

About how many whole miles is that? _____

g. Anthony walks 950 ft to school every morning. Figure out how many feet he walks to and from school in a five-day school week.

_____

About how many whole miles is that? _____

Metric Units for Measuring Length

The basic unit for measuring length in the metric system is **the meter**. All the other units are based on the meter, and in fact, have the word "meter" in them.

Each unit in the metric system is 10 times the smaller unit. For example, 1 kilometer is 10 hectometers and 1 centimeter is 10 millimeters. However, we don't commonly use hectometers, dekameters, or decimeters. You need to learn only the units that are bolded in the chart.

Units of length in the metric system

kilometer	**km**	"Kilo" means 1,000.
hectometer	hm	(not used)
dekameter	dam	(not used)
meter	**m**	**the basic unit**
decimeter	dm	(not used much)
centimeter	**cm**	This is 1/100 of a meter.
millimeter	**mm**	This is 1/10 of a centimeter.

10, 10, 10, 10, 10, 10, 10

Remember also that **1 meter is very close to 1 yard**. One meter is just a bit longer than one yard.

1. Draw two lines at least 4 m long that start at the same place (outside, in a hallway, or a large room).

   a. On the one line, make marks for 1 m, 2 m, 3 m, and 4 m. Then try to take "hops" one meter long.

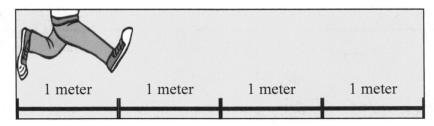

   1 meter   1 meter   1 meter   1 meter

   b. On the second line make marks at each foot, from 1 to 13 feet. Then take 1-yard hops.

   Do the two kinds of hops feel about the same?

2. Measure how tall you and other people are in centimeters. Write it also using whole meters and centimeters.

Name	Height
	_____ cm = _1_ m _____ cm.

Conversions between units

Remember what millimeters look like on a ruler. They are tiny! **Ten millimeters make 1 cm.**

Then verify from a measuring tape that **100 centimeters makes one meter.** "Centi" means one hundred (from the Latin word *centum*). That is why 1 dollar has 100 *cents*, and 1 meter has 100 *centi*meters.

Lastly, **1 kilometer is 1,000 meters**, because "kilo" means one thousand.

1 km = 1,000 m	1 m = 100 cm	1 cm = 10 mm

3. One meter is 100 cm. Convert between meters and centimeters.

a. 5 m = _____ cm	**b.** 4 m 6 cm = _____ cm	**c.** 800 cm = _____ m
8 m = _____ cm	9 m 19 cm = _____ cm	239 cm = ____ m _____ cm
12 m = _____ cm	10 m 80 cm = _____ cm	407 cm = ____ m _____ cm

4. One centimeter is 10 mm. Convert between centimeters and millimeters.

a. 5 cm = _____ mm	**b.** 2 cm 8 mm = _____ mm	**c.** 50 mm = ____ cm _____ mm
8 cm = _____ mm	7 cm 5 mm = _____ mm	72 mm = ____ cm _____ mm
14 cm = _____ mm	10 cm 4 mm = _____ mm	145 mm = ____ cm _____ mm

5. One kilometer is 1,000 m. Convert between kilometers and meters.

a. 5 km = _____ m	**b.** 2 km 800 m = _____ m	**c.** 2,000 m = _____ km
23 km = _____ m	6 km 50 m = _____ m	4,300 m = ____ km _____ m
1 km 200 m = _____ m	13 km 579 m = _____ m	18,700 m = ____ km _____ m

6. Calculate. Give your answer using whole kilometers and meters.

  a. 5 km 200 m + 8 km 900 m

  b. 3 km 600 m + 2 km 800 m

  c. 1,500 m + 2 km 600 m

  d. 6 × 700 m

7. Solve.

a. Find the perimeter of this rectangle.

2 m

80 cm

b. Find the perimeter of this rectangle.

7 mm

1 cm 5 mm

c. One side of a square measures 5 cm 6 mm. What is its perimeter?

d. *A challenge.* A square has a perimeter of 6 cm. How long is its side?

8. Solve the problems.

a. How many millimeters are in a *meter*?

b. John jogs around a track 1 km 800 m long twice a day, five days a week.
How long a distance does he jog in a day?

In a week?

c. Gary is 1 m 34 cm tall and Jared is 142 cm tall.
How much taller is Jared?

Kathy's wallpaper has butterflies that are 8 cm wide. She will put the wallpaper in her room. How many complete butterflies can she have on a wall that is 1 meter long?

How about if the wall is 3 meters long?

Puzzle Corner

Customary Units of Weight

Units of weight in the customary system

2,000 → (short) **ton** — **T** — to measure very heavy things

16 → **pound** — **lb** — to measure medium-heavy things

ounce — **oz** — to measure light things

1. Measure light items with a kitchen scale. Write your results here.

Item	Weight
	_____ lb _____ oz

2. Choose the right weight for each thing. Sometimes there are two possibilities.

a. a sparrow	b. a book	c. an elephant
10 oz 1 oz 16 oz	1 lb 2 oz 20 oz	40 oz 40 lb 4 T
d. a car	**e. a magazine**	**f. a healthy woman**
2 T 3,500 lb 300 lb	5 oz 2 lb 1 lb	80 lb 130 lb 60 lb
g. a tractor	**h. a 3-year old boy**	**i. a fridge**
200 T 3 T 140 lb	22 lb 44 lb 66 lb	7 lb 200 lb 1 T

3. One pound is 16 ounces. One ton is 2,000 pounds. Fill in the tables.

Pounds	1/2	1	2	2 1/2	3	4	5
Ounces							

Tons	2	3	4	5	10	12	20
Pounds							

1 lb = 16 oz
To change 6 pounds into ounces, multiply by 16: 6×16 oz = 96 oz.
To change 3 lb 11 oz into ounces, first convert the 3 pounds into ounces: 3×16 oz = 48 oz.   Then, add the 11 ounces: 48 oz $+ 11$ oz = 59 oz.

4. Convert pounds and ounces to ounces.

a. 2 lb = _____ oz	**b.** 1 lb 1 oz = _____ oz	**c.** 4 lb 4 oz = _____ oz
3 lb = _____ oz	5 lb 5 oz = _____ oz	2 lb 13 oz = _____ oz
4 lb = _____ oz	3 lb 11 oz = _____ oz	5 lb 3 oz = _____ oz

5. Newborn twin babies weighed 7 lb 13 oz and 8 lb.
   How much heavier was the second baby?

6. Farmer Smith's red apples weigh about 4 oz each.
   How many red apples are in 1 lb of apples?
   In 5 lb of apples?

7. An ounce of rice costs $0.09.
   Find the price for 2 pounds of rice.

8. Janet weighed some cocoa powder on the scales. It weighed 2 lb 5 oz.
   Janet put some of the cocoa powder in a bag. Now the scales show 1 lb 8 oz.
   How much cocoa powder did she put in the bag?

To change 35 oz into pounds and ounces, think how many 16-ounce "chunks" are in the 35 ounces. Each 16 ounces makes 1 pound: 35 oz = 16 oz $+ 16$ oz $+ 3$ oz. So, 35 oz is 2 lb 3 oz.

9. Convert ounces to pounds and ounces.

a. 17 oz = _____ lb _____ oz	**b.** 32 oz = _____ lb _____ oz	**c.** 51 oz = _____ lb _____ oz
19 oz = _____ lb _____ oz	35 oz = _____ lb _____ oz	55 oz = _____ lb _____ oz
23 oz = _____ lb _____ oz	46 oz = _____ lb _____ oz	60 oz = _____ lb _____ oz

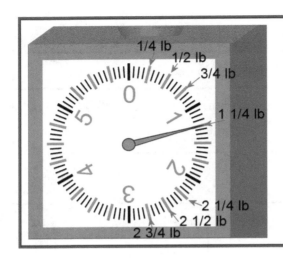

The pound can be divided into four equal parts. Each part is 4 ounces. The longer, red marks on the scales are for 4, 8, and 12 ounces.

- 1/4 pound = 4 ounces
- 1/2 pound = 8 ounces
- 3/4 pound = 12 ounces
- 1 pound = 16 ounces

The scale on the left shows 2 pounds and 4 ounces. We can also say it is 2 1/4 pounds.

10. Write the weight using pounds and ounces, and also using fractional parts of a pound.

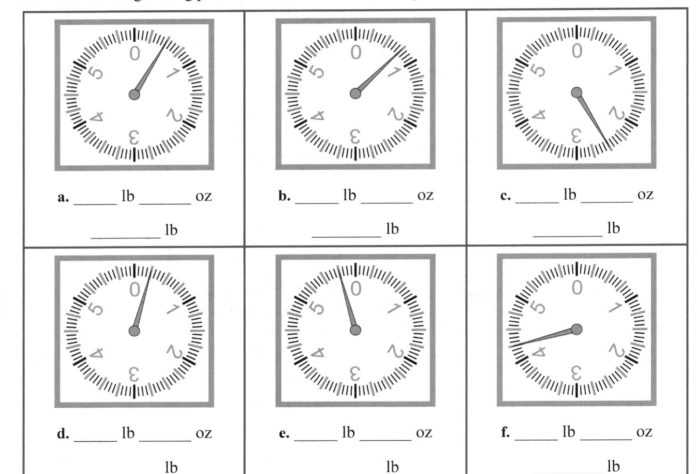

a. _____ lb _____ oz

_____ lb

b. _____ lb _____ oz

_____ lb

c. _____ lb _____ oz

_____ lb

d. _____ lb _____ oz

_____ lb

e. _____ lb _____ oz

_____ lb

f. _____ lb _____ oz

_____ lb

11. Convert fractional parts of a pound into ounces.

a. 1/2 lb = _____ oz	**b.** 1/4 lb = _____ oz	**c.** 3/4 lb = _____ oz
1 1/2 lb = _____ oz	2 1/4 lb = _____ oz	1 3/4 lb = _____ oz

Adding in columns, you can add pounds to pounds and ounces to ounces. Afterwards, check if the sum of ounces makes some additional pounds.

In the example on the right, 33 oz gives us two additional pounds, because 33 oz = 16 oz + 16 oz + 1 oz. We add those 2 lb to the sum of the pounds (3 lb). So, 3 lb 33 oz becomes 5 lb 1 oz.

```
              9 oz
      1 lb  11 oz
   +  2 lb  13 oz
   ─────────────────
      3 lb  33 oz

   = 5 lb   1 oz
```

12. Add.

a.	b.	c.	d.
1 lb 8 oz + 7 oz	2 lb 2 oz + 4 lb 9 oz	6 lb 8 oz 2 lb 12 oz + 1 lb 13 oz	2 lb 6 oz 1 lb 5 oz + 4 lb 9 oz
=	=	=	=

13. Solve.

a. Jose's packages and letters for the week weighed
2 oz, 6 oz, 5 oz, 1 lb 1 oz, and 1 lb 4 oz.
What was their total weight?

b. Mary ate 1/4 lb of bread, and Jessie ate 7 ounces of bread.
Who ate more?

How much more?

c. Two children weighed some of their stuffed animals.
These are the weights: 4 oz, 6 oz, 5 oz, 11 oz, 1 lb 3 oz, and 8 oz.
Find the total weight of the stuffed animals.

d. A bag of split peas weighs 1 lb 4 oz.
How much do four bags of split peas weigh?

Ten bags?

Metric Units of Weight

In the metric system, each unit is 10 of the smaller unit. For example, 1 dekagram is 10 grams, and 1 kilogram is 10 hectograms. But dekagrams and hectograms are not commonly used. We only use kilograms and grams.

You just need to remember that **1 kg = 1,000 g**. The word "kilo" actually means a thousand!

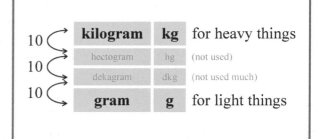

1. Choose the right weight for each thing.

a. a 10-year old boy	b. a cat	c. an apple
1 kg 30 g 30 kg	2 kg 200 g 2,000 g	1 kg 100 g 1 g
d. a table	**e. a pencil**	**f. an adult woman**
2 kg 200 g 20 kg	5 g 5 kg 500 g	50 kg 200 kg 5 kg

2. One kilogram is a thousand grams. Fill in the table.

kilograms	1/2	2	3	3 1/2	5	10	12
grams							

kilograms							
grams	500	1,000	4,000	4,500	6,000	10,000	40,000

1 kg = 1,000 g
To change 3 kg into grams, multiply by 1,000: $3 \times 1,000 \text{ g} = 3,000 \text{ g}$
To change 5 kg 50 g into grams, first convert the 5 kg into grams: $5 \times 1,000 \text{ g} = 5,000 \text{ g}$. Then, add the 50 grams: $5,000 \text{ g} + 50 \text{ g} = 5,050 \text{ g}$.

3. Convert between kilograms and grams.

a. 2 kg = _____ g	b. 1 kg 600 g = _____ g	c. 8 kg 600 g = _____ g
3 kg = _____ g	8 kg 80 g = _____ g	5 kg 8 g = _____ g
4 kg = _____ g	2 kg 450 g = _____ g	7 kg 41 g = _____ g

4. Convert the amounts in grams into kilograms and grams.

a. 6,000 g = _____ kg _____ g	**b.** 1,200 g = _____ kg _____ g
6,700 g = _____ kg _____ g	6,070 g = _____ kg _____ g
5,300 g = _____ kg _____ g	4,770 g = _____ kg _____ g

5. Circle the heaviest amount.

a. 3 kg 300 g OR 3,030 g	**b.** 6 kg 400 g OR 640 g	**c.** 10 kg OR 5,000 g

6. Apples weigh about 150 grams each. Grandma wants about 1 kg of apples.
   How many apples should she get?

7. How many workbooks weighing 300 g each can you pack
   into a box so that its weight will not be over 2 kg?

8. Which is more chocolate: five chocolate bars 400 g each,
   or two jumbo chocolate bars 1 kg each?

When some weights are given in kilograms and some in grams, you can change them all to grams before adding.		Add kilograms to kilograms and grams to grams. Here, 1,050 g makes 1 kg 50 g.
5 kg + 3 kg 650 g + 490 g = ? Change to grams first: = 5,000 g + 3,650 g + 490 g = 9,140 g OR 9 kg 140 g	$$\begin{array}{r} 5\ 0\ 0\ 0 \\ 3\ 6\ 5\ 0 \\ +\ \ \ 4\ 9\ 0 \\ \hline 9\ 1\ 4\ 0 \end{array}$$	$$\begin{array}{r} 4\ \text{kg} \quad 250\ \text{g} \\ +\ 3\ \text{kg} \quad 800\ \text{g} \\ \hline 7\ \text{kg}\ \ 1050\ \text{g} \\[4pt] =\ 8\ \text{kg} \quad \ \ 50\ \text{g} \end{array}$$

9. Add.

a. $\begin{array}{r} 1\ \text{kg} \quad 820\ \text{g} \\ +\ 5\ \text{kg} \quad 700\ \text{g} \\ \hline \\ = \end{array}$	**b.** 7 kg 800 g + 4,200 g	**c.** 4,150 g + 3 kg 60 g + 600 g

10. Calculate.

a.	b.
1 kg 700 g + 4 kg 200 g = _____ kg _____ g	4 × 300 g = _____ kg _____ g
1,500 g + 500 g = _____ kg _____ g	4 × 500 g = _____ kg _____ g
4 kg 800 g + 4 kg 400 g = _____ kg _____ g	2 kg − 900 g = _____ kg _____ g

11. Jeremy received packages in the mail that weighed
    700 g, 350 g, 4 kg 400 g, and 1 kg 900 g.
    What was the total weight of the packages?

12. Angie bought three 1-kg packages and seven
    400-gram packages of buckwheat flour.
    How much did the flour weigh in total?

13. You need 2 kg of flour to make bread. The scale
    shows you already have 1,050 g.
    How much more flour do you need?

14. A 200-gram bag of millet costs $1.69.
    How many bags do you need for 1 kg of millet?
    What is the total cost?

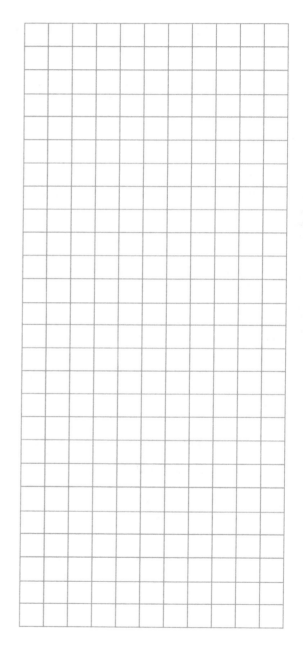

Customary Units of Volume

Volume has to do with **how much space** something takes up.

You are already familiar with **cups, pints, quarts, and gallons**. They are units for measuring volume in the customary system.

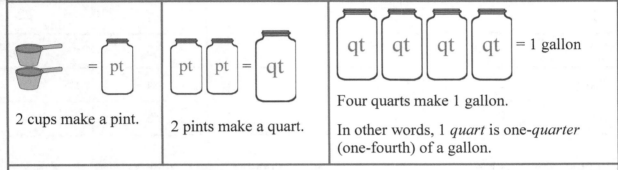

2 cups make a pint.

2 pints make a quart.

Four quarts make 1 gallon.

In other words, 1 *quart* is one-*quarter* (one-fourth) of a gallon.

Besides those, we use **fluid ounces** to measure small volumes. Notice that fluid ounces are different from the ounces used to measure weight. Fluid ounces are abbreviated with "fl. oz." or just "oz" if there is no possibility of confusing them with the other ounces.

Units of volume in the customary system

4	**gallon**	for large amounts of liquid (gal)
	quart	for medium-size amounts of liquid (qt)
2	**pint**	for medium-size amounts of liquid (pt)
2	**cup**	for small amounts of liquid (C)
8	**ounce**	for small amounts of liquid (oz.)

1. Find 1-cup, 1/2-cup, and 1/4-cup measuring cups (used in baking). Then, find the markings on them that are for ounces.

   a. Measure 1 ounce of water into a drinking glass.

   b. Measure 2 ounces of water into a drinking glass.

   c. Measure 4 ounces of water into a drinking glass.

   d. Guess how many ounces of water would fit into the drinking glass. Then check.

   e. Guess how many ounces of water would fit into a food container. Then check.

f. Fill in.

Cups	Ounces
1/2	
1	
1 1/2	
2	
3	

195

2. Fill in.

a.			b.			c.	
Quarts	**Cups**		**Quarts**	**Pints**		**Gallons**	**Quarts**
1/2			1/4			1/2	
1			1/2			1	
2			1			2	
3			2			3	
4			3			4	
5			4			5	

3. Fill in the blanks with the words "quart(s)", "pint(s)", "cup(s)", and "gallon(s)".

a. pt pt = 1 _____

b. qt = 4 _____

c. pt = 2 _____

d. qt pt = 3 _____

e. = 1 _____

f. qt = 2 _____

g.  = 1 _____

h. pt pt = 4 _____

i. qt qt qt qt = 1 _____

j. pt pt pt pt = 2 _____

4. Convert without pictures.

a.	b.	c.	d.
1 pt = _____ C	1 qt = _____ C	1 gal = _____ qt	2 qt = _____ pt
1/2 pt = _____ C	1/4 qt = _____ C	3 gal = _____ qt	3 qt = _____ C

5. Solve.

a. Margie drank two cups of coffee. How many ounces is that?

b. A big shampoo bottle contains 20 fluid ounces. Another contains a pint.
   Which one contains more shampoo?

c. Mom filled a child's toy bucket from a 1-quart jar full of water.
   After that, 1 cup of water remained in the jar.
   How much water did the bucket hold?

d. How many 4-ounce servings can you get from 1 cup of juice?

   How many 4-ounce servings can you get from 3 cups of juice?

   How many 6-ounce servings can you get from 3 cups of juice?

e. Which is more, a 32-ounce jumbo drink, or 3 cups of water?

f. A washing machine uses 20 gallons of water for one wash cycle.
   How many quarts is that?

   A bucket holds 10 quarts. How many buckets of water would you
   need to fill the washing machine?

g. If you fill a 5-gallon bucket with water using a 1-quart container,
   how many times do you need to fill the container?

h. Mom used 1 quart of milk from a 1/2-gallon milk jug in cooking. How much is left?

Metric Units of Volume

The most common units of volume in the metric system are **liters** and **milliliters**.

A **liter** is very close to a quart; it is just a little bit more. A liter is usually abbreviated "L" but sometimes you may see just a lowercase "l."

Milliliters are thousandth parts of a liter. In other words, **1,000 milliliters make one liter.** A milliliter is abbreviated "ml."

Most measuring cups have a milliliter scale.
Two cups is about 500 ml. Four cups, or a quart, is about 1 L.

Units of volume in the metric system

$1 L = 1,000 ml$

liter	**L**	for larger amounts of liquid
deciliter	dl	(for medium amounts of liquid)
centiliter	cl	(for small amounts of liquid)
milliliter	**ml**	for small amounts of liquid

(10, 10, 10)

1. The measuring cup can hold 500 ml when full. Color the cup to fill it to the correct measurement.

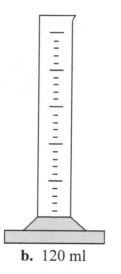
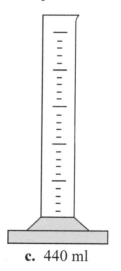
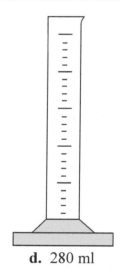

a. 300 ml   **b.** 120 ml   **c.** 440 ml   **d.** 280 ml

2. Underline the correct amount.

    a. An eye dropper can hold (5/500) milliliters.

    b. Three cups of flour is about (75/750) ml.

    c. A bucket of water is about (10/100) liters.

    d. A quart of juice is about (1/3) liters.

    e. A glass of milk is about (20/200) ml.

    f. The gas tank of a car holds (80/800) L of gas.

1 L = 1,000 ml
To change 4 L into milliliters, multiply by 1,000: $4 \times 1{,}000$ ml = 4,000 ml
To change 2 L 250 ml into milliliters, first convert the 2 L into milliliters: $2 \times 1{,}000$ ml = 2,000 ml. Then, add the 250 milliliters: 2,000 ml + 250 ml = 2,250 ml.

3. Fill in the tables.

L	1/2	1	1 1/2	2	5	12
ml						

L						
ml	2,500	3,000	4,500	8,000	10,000	20,000

4. Convert between liters and milliliters.

a.	b.	c.
2 L = _____ ml 6 L = _____ ml	1 L 200 ml = _____ ml 4 L 230 ml = _____ ml	7 L 70 ml = _____ ml 4 L 330 ml = _____ ml
d.	e.	f.
3,000 ml = _____ L 10,000 ml = _____ L	4,300 ml = _____ L _____ ml 9,880 ml = _____ L _____ ml	3,040 ml = _____ L _____ ml 5,053 ml = _____ L _____ ml

5. Solve.

a. Jeanine drank 250 ml of a 1-liter bottle of juice.
   How much is left?

b. Mark filled four 200-ml glasses from a 2-liter bottle of juice.
   How much is left now?

c. How many 200-ml glasses can you fill with 1 liter of water?

   How about from a 5-liter water cooler?

d. A 250-ml cup of yogurt costs $1.20. You bought enough of
   them to equal one liter of yogurt. How much did that cost?

You can add liters to liters, and milliliters to milliliters.	$\begin{array}{r} 2 \text{ L} \quad 650 \text{ ml} \\ + \; 1 \text{ L} \quad 700 \text{ ml} \\ \hline 3 \text{ L} \quad 1350 \text{ ml} \\[4pt] = 4 \text{ L} \quad 350 \text{ ml} \end{array}$
In the end, check if the sum of the milliliters is more than 1,000 ml. If so, you get some whole liters from that.	

6. Add.

a. $\begin{array}{r} 1 \text{ L} \quad 800 \text{ ml} \\ 650 \text{ ml} \\ + \; 2 \text{ L} \quad 700 \text{ ml} \\ \hline \end{array}$ $=$	**b.** 5 L 200 ml + 2,500 ml 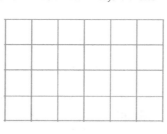	**c.** 450 ml + 450 ml + 2 L 150 ml 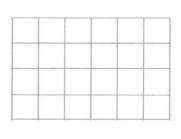

7. Calculate in your head. Just remember that 1 liter is 1,000 ml!

a.	b.
3 L 700 ml + 700 ml = _____ L _____ ml	5 L − 600 ml = _____ L _____ ml
6 L 800 ml + 2 L 400 ml = _____ L _____ ml	4 L − 2 L 300 ml = _____ L _____ ml

8. During his workday, Matt consumed 1 1/2 liters of water, 400 ml of coffee, and 200 ml of juice. What was the total volume of the liquids he drank?

9. Jeanine bought five 250-ml cans of juice, two 2-liter bottles of water, and three 350-ml bottles of juice. Find the total amount of liquid in liters and milliliters.

10. A 150 ml container of yogurt costs $0.78. If you buy enough of them to equal a little over one liter, how much does that cost?

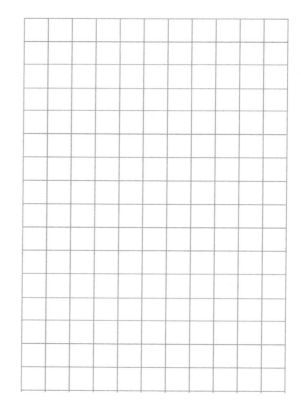

Mixed Review Chapter 4

1. Fill in the missing numbers. Write the area of the *whole* rectangle as a sum of the areas of the *smaller* rectangles. Also find the total area. (Multiply in Parts—Area Model/Ch.3)

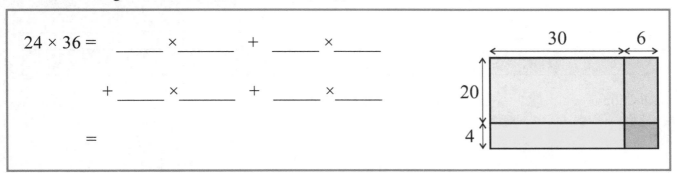

24 × 36 = _____ × _____ + _____ × _____

+ _____ × _____ + _____ × _____

=

2. Multiply. First, estimate the final answer.

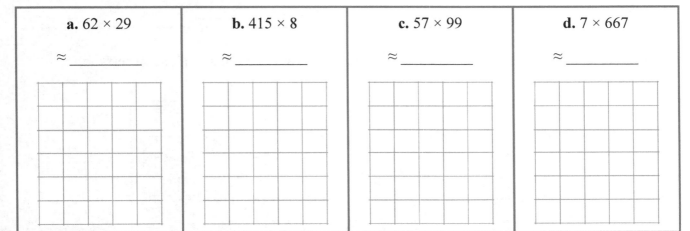

a. 62 × 29	**b.** 415 × 8	**c.** 57 × 99	**d.** 7 × 667
≈ _____	≈ _____	≈ _____	≈ _____

3. Solve.

a. Andrew gets paid $65 weekly for a part-time job.
There are 52 weeks in a year but he takes off four
weeks each year from work.
How much does he earn in a year?

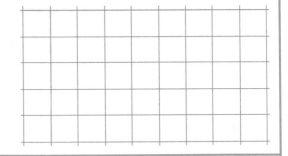

b. The distance from Steven's home to his job is 24 km.
He drives to work and back every day, five days a week.
How many kilometers does he drive in a 5-day work week?

_____

_____

4. Write the numbers *and x* in the bar model. Remember, *x* is the unknown: what the problem asks for. Write an addition using the numbers and *x*. Lastly solve. (Bar Models in Addition and Subtraction/Ch.1)

a. Madison made tortillas. She sold 16 of them to a neighbor, 20 to another, and then had 12 left. How many tortillas did she make?	**b.** Emma bought three books for $12 each and a computer part. The total bill was $73. How much did the computer part cost?
Addition:	Addition:
Solution: *x* = _____	Solution: *x* = _____

5. The graph shows the weekly income from the sale of strawberries on a small strawberry farm. (Line Graphs/Ch.1)

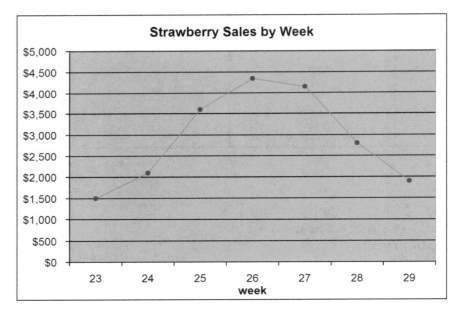

a. What week did the farm sell the most strawberries?

   About how much were the sales that week?

b. What week did the farm sell the least strawberries?

   About how much were the sales that week?

c. Estimate the total sales for the weeks 25-27.

Review Chapter 4

1. How much time passes?

   a. From 11:15 p.m. till 6:07 a.m.

   b. From 10:55 till 21:35.

2. A flight that lasts 4 hours 20 minutes took off at 1:50 p.m.
   When does it land?

3. Describe a situation to fit these temperatures.

   a. 25°F

   b. 25°C

4. Draw a line that is...

   a. 2 3/8 in. long

   b. 36 mm long

5. Convert between the different measuring units.

a. 15 cm = _____ mm	**b.** 4 yd = _____ ft	**c.** 4 m 25 cm = _____ cm
6 cm 8 mm = _____ mm	5 ft 8 in. = _____ in.	8 km = _____ m

6. The sides of a rectangle measure 2 ft 8 in. and 5 ft 9 in.
   What is its perimeter?

7. The distance from Sarah's home to the community center
   is 1 km 400 m. If Sarah goes there *and back* twice a week,
   what distance does she walk in total?

8. Choose the right weight for each thing. Sometimes there are two possibilities.

a. a 5-year old child	**b.** a thick dictionary	**c.** a letter
16 kg 12 lb 34 lb	8 oz 2 kg 12 oz	2 lb 2 oz 20 oz

9. Convert between the units of weight.

a. 7 lb = _____ oz	**b.** 3 T 200 lb = _____ lb	**c.** 2 1/2 kg = _____ g
5 lb 11 oz = _____ oz	7 kg 500 g = _____ g	3,456 g = ____ kg _____ g

10. At his doctor visit, Matthew weighed 23 kg 200 g.
    He had gained 2 kg 350 g since his last visit.
    What did he weigh at his previous visit?

11. Mary gives her cat 6 oz of cat food every day.
    How many days will the 2-lb sack of cat food last?

12. Which is more?

a. 3 gal 11 qt	**b.** 21 fl. oz. 3 cups	**c.** 3 pints 1/2 gallon

13. Convert between units of volume.

a.	**b.**	**c.**
2 L 300 ml = _____ ml	3 qt = _____ pt	4 gal = _____ qt
6,550 ml = ____ L _____ ml	3 qt = _____ cups	2 cups = _____ fl. oz.

14. Alice and Sheila made 3 gallons of punch for a party.
    How many cups of punch will it provide?

A special medicinal honey costs $2.00 per
fluid ounce, and Samantha bought a quart.
How much did she pay?

Puzzle Corner